Off By Heart

Off By Heart

ff By Heart

f By Heart

ff By Heart

ff By Heart

ff By Heart

Off By Heart

Foreword by Michael Rosen

Edited by Daisy Goodwin

First published in 2009 by Scholastic Children's Books
An imprint of Scholastic Ltd
Euston House, 24 Eversholt Street
London, NW1 1DB, UK
Registered office: Westfield Road, Southam, Warwickshire, CV47 0RA
SCHOLASTIC and associated logos are trademarks and/or registered trade-
marks of Scholastic Inc.

ISBN 978 1407 11208 4

Printed by Bookmarque Ltd, Croydon, Surrey.
Papers used by Scholastic Children's Books are made from wood grown in
sustainable forests.

1 3 5 7 9 10 8 6 4 2

www.scholastic.co.uk/zone

Contents

Foreword
by Michael Rosen

I think getting to know a poem off by heart and finding a way of performing it is a great way to get to the heart of what a poem is about. The process of learning and performing is a way of getting to feel a poem. The business of 'getting' a poem isn't just a matter of understanding or 'comprehension'. It's very important to know it through feeling it.

Any poem is good to know well. Some are easier and catchier to keep hold of, particularly if they have a rhythm or if the phrases in the poem echo each other in some way. They don't have to rhyme. For hundreds of years, people in this country learned the psalms or other parts of the Bible, where the phrases and verses of the Bible have a rhythm or what musicians call a 'cadence'. Many people could learn these quite easily.

So, if you want to find a poem to perform, first find one that you like the feel of; second, read it again and again and again; third, start reciting it in front of other people and watch them as you do it, seeing how they react to the poem as it unfolds. If at any point they appear bored or distracted, see if you can think of doing something differently with that part of the poem to keep people's attention. Don't forget that you have many tools to perform a poem with: your voice, your eyes, the movements and expressions on your face, the movements of your hands and arms, walking, jumping, hopping, running, and the rhythms you can create with movements of your whole body - swaying, turning.

Finally, remember that you can think of your voice as a body which can run fast or slow, it can do little darting movements, big slow movements, it can glide, or be jerky, it can leap high, it can sink low. Any part of a poem will match one of these movements. As an experiment, you can try saying the same line of a poem in very different ways - slow, fast, loud, soft, gliding, jerky and see what these different sounds feel like.

So pick up a poem and feeeeeel it! Enjoy!

How to Remember a Poem
Here are three different techniques to help you memorize a poem.

1: Image Association

   (In other words, think of a picture!)

- Break the poem down into little segments, or beats, which express a common theme, movement or emotion.
- Practise the poem in these chunks.
- Have a single image or emotion that reminds you of a particular chunk.
- Have an overall image that reminds you of the whole poem, bringing all the smaller chunks of information together.
- Recalling the overall image should trigger you to remember the different images in the order that they come in the poem.

2: Benjamin Franklin's Technique

   (As recommended by the great American inventor and founding father.)

- Break the poem down into four-line segments or into single phrases.
- Write down the gist of the phrase in your own words
- Have a ten-second pause.

- Then try and recreate the actual line from what you've written down.
- Think about what extra things the poet is doing that you didn't notice at first – why he's chosen particular words, for their rhyme or rhythm. Trying to perceive the reasons behind these choices should lodge the lines in your memory and help you understand them.

3: Spatial Association
   (In other words, make connections!)

- Take a room in your house. For each place in it, associate a few lines of the poem with a particular object – your bed might be the first two, your wardrobe the next two, your window the next two and so on.
- Say the poem as you walk around your room, pausing by each significant object.
- To remember the poem, imagine walking round the room in the order that the trigger objects appear in the poem.

This technique also works well with a familiar journey: for instance, your route to school, where the objects you associate with lines might be particular trees, buildings or shops.

Remember, your memory is like a muscle: the more you use it, the stronger it will grow. And that applies to adults as well as children; just don't be discouraged if you find it harder to learn poems word perfectly than your kids.

The Rhythm of Life
Michael Rosen

Hand on the bridge
feel the rhythm of the train
Hand on the bridge
feel the rhythm of the rain
Hand on your throat
feel the rhythm of your talk
Hand on your leg
feel the rhythm of your walk
Hand in the sea
feel the rhythm of the tide
Hand on your heart
feel the rhythm inside
Hand on the rhythm
feel the rhythm of the rhyme
Hand on your life
feel the rhythm of time
Hand your life
feel the rhythm of time
Hand on your life
feel the rhythm of time

Section 1

Hop

Hop into a short, easy poem!

The Eagle
Alfred, Lord Tennyson

He clasps the crag with crooked hands;
Close to the sun in lonely lands,
Ring'd with the azure world, he stands.

The wrinkled sea beneath him crawls;
He watches from his mountain walls,
And like a thunderbolt he falls.

This is the perfect poem to learn and recite aloud – especially on a mountaintop!

I Don't Want To Go Into School
Colin McNaughton

I don't want to go into school today, Mum,
I don't feel like schoolwork today.
Oh, don't make me go to school today, Mum
Oh, please let me stay home and play.

But you must go to school, my cherub, my lamb.
If you don't it will be a disaster,
How would they manage without you, my sweet,
After all, you are the headmaster!

And here's one for when you want to stay at home. . .

The Sick Rose
William Blake

O Rose, thou art sick!
The invisible worm
That flies in the night,
In the howling storm,

Has found out thy bed
Of crimson joy;
And his dark secret love
Does thy life destroy.

One of England's greatest poets wrote this. What do you think it means?

How Doth the Little Crocodile
Lewis Carroll

How doth the little crocodile
Improve his shining tail,
And pour the waters of the Nile
On every golden scale!
How cheerfully he seems to grin,
How neatly spreads his claws,
And welcomes little fishes in
With gently smiling jaws!

A poem with a twist in its tail!

The Common Cormorant
Christopher Isherwood

The common cormorant (or shag)
Lays eggs inside a paper bag,
You follow the idea, no doubt?
It's to keep the lightning out.

But what these unobservant birds
Have never thought of, is that herds
Of wandering bears might come with buns
And steal the bags to hold the crumbs.

Jenny Kissed Me
Leigh Hunt

Jenny kiss'd me when we met,
    Jumping from the chair she sat in;
Time, you thief, who love to get
    Sweets into your list, put that in!
Say I'm weary, say I'm sad,
    Say that health and wealth have miss'd me;
Say I'm growing old, but add,
    Jenny kiss'd me!

"A slash of Blue"
Emily Dickinson

A slash of Blue—
A sweep of Gray—
Some scarlet patches on the way,
Compose an Evening Sky—
A little purple — slipped between—
Some Ruby Trousers hurried on—
A Wave of Gold—
A Bank of Day—
This just makes out the Morning Sky.

Some people think this might be a poem about the American Civil War because one army wore blue and the other grey.

Stickleback
Ted Hughes

The stickleback's a spiky chap,
Worse than a bit of a briar.
Hungry Pike would sooner swallow
Embers from a fire.

The stickleback is fearless in
The way he loves his wife.
Every minute of the day
He guards her with his life.

She, like him, is dressed to kill
In stiff and steely prickles,
And when they kiss, there bubbles up
The laughter of the tickles.

A fishy poem!

The Night is Darkening Round Me
Emily Brontë

The night is darkening round me,
   The wild winds coldly blow;
But a tyrant spell has bound me
   And I cannot, cannot go.

The giant trees are bending
   Their bare boughs weighed with snow,
The storm is fast descending
   And yet I cannot go.

Clouds beyond clouds above me,
   Wastes beyond wastes below;
But nothing drear can move me;
   I will not, cannot go.

The Lamplighter
Robert Louis Stevenson

My tea is nearly ready and the sun has left the sky.
It's time to take the window to see Leerie going by;
For every night at teatime and before you take your seat,
With lantern and with ladder he comes posting up the street.

Now Tom would be a driver and Maria go to sea,
And my papa's a banker and as rich as he can be;
But I, when I am stronger and can choose what I'm to do,
O Leerie, I'll go round at night and light the lamps with you!

For we are very lucky, with a lamp before the door,
And Leerie stops to light it as he lights so many more;
And O! before you hurry by with ladder and with light,
O Leerie, see a little child and nod to him to-night!

"Leerie" the lamplighter lit the gas lamps in the streets of Edinburgh where Stevenson lived.

"maggie and milly and molly and may"
e.e. cummings

maggie and milly and molly and may
went down to the beach(to play one day)

and maggie discovered a shell that sang
so sweetly she couldn't remember her troubles,and

milly befriended a stranded star
whose rays five languid fingers were;

and molly was chased by a horrible thing
which raced sideways while blowing bubbles:and

may came home with a smooth round stone
as small as a world and as large as alone.

For whatever we lose(like a you or a me)
it's always ourselves we find in the sea

Shout this out as loud as you can next time you're at the beach!

13

The Garden Seat
Thomas Hardy

Its former green is blue and thin,
And its once firm legs sink in and in;
Soon it will break down unaware,
Soon it will break down unaware.

At night when reddest flowers are black
Those who once sat thereon come back;
Quite a row of them sitting there,
Quite a row of them sitting there.

With them the seat does not break down,
Nor winter freeze them, nor floods drown,
For they are as light as upper air,
They are as light as upper air!

*The poet Seamus Heaney first heard this read by Ted
Hughes. He says, "Almost immediately I found it lodged in
my memory – maybe because of its song-like quality, which
comes from the repetition of the third line of each stanza,
maybe because of a very definite pattern of stress pattern*

in all the lines. I also found myself repeating it to my seven-year-old daughter as we drove to school and was delighted that after a couple of mornings she too had it by heart."

Travel
Edna St Vincent Millay

The railroad track is miles away,
   And the day is loud with voices speaking,
Yet there isn't a train goes by all day
   But I hear its whistle shrieking.

All night there isn't a train goes by,
   Though the night is still for sleep and dreaming,
But I see its cinders red on the sky,
   And hear its engine steaming.

My heart is warm with friends I make,
   And better friends I'll not be knowing;
Yet there isn't a train I wouldn't take,
   No matter where it's going.

The poet Roger McGough chose this, because of "the feeling it evokes of yearning, of wanting to be elsewhere, even though we may be happy here. A child could identify with this".

Teeth
Spike Milligan

English Teeth, English Teeth!
Shining in the sun
A part of British heritage
Aye, each and every one.

English Teeth, Happy Teeth!
Always having fun
Clamping down on bits of fish
And sausages half done.

English Teeth! HEROES' Teeth!
Hear them click! and clack!
Let's sing a song of praise to them –
Three Cheers for the Brown Grey and Black.

Learn a poem by the master of comic verse.

" 'Tis moonlight "
Emily Brontë

'Tis moonlight, summer moonlight,
All soft and still and fair;
The solemn hour of midnight
Breathes sweet thoughts everywhere,

But most where trees are sending
Their breezy boughs on high,
Or stooping low are lending
A shelter from the sky.

And there in those wild bowers
A lovely form is laid;
Green grass and dew-steeped flowers
Wave gently round her head.

Sea-Fever
John Masefield

I must go down to the seas again, to the lonely sea and the sky,
And all I ask is a tall ship and a star to steer her by,
And the wheel's kick and the wind's song and the white
    sail's shaking,
And a grey mist on the sea's face and a grey dawn breaking.

I must go down to the seas again, for the call of the running tide
Is a wild call and a clear call that may not be denied;
And all I ask is a windy day with the white clouds flying,
And the flung spray and the blown spume, and the
    sea-gulls crying.

I must go down to the seas again, to the vagrant gypsy life,
To the gull's way and the whale's way where the wind's like
    a whetted knife;
And all I ask is a merry yarn from a laughing fellow-rover
And quiet sleep and a sweet dream when the long trick's over.

Daisy Goodwin says, "My grandmother used to read this poem to me when I was a child. It is one of those irresistible combinations of sound and meaning that makes any adventure seem possible."

The Frog
Hilaire Belloc

Be kind and tender to the Frog,
And do not call him names;
As "Slimy skin", or "Polly-wog",
Or likewise "Ugly James",
Or "Gap-a-grin", or "Toad-gone-wrong",
Or "Bill Bandy-knees":
The Frog is justly sensitive
To epithets like these.

No animal will more repay
A treatment kind and fair;
At least so lonely people say,
Who keep a frog (and, by the way
They are extremely rare).

The Sun Has Long Been Set
William Wordsworth

The sun has long been set,
The stars are out by twos and threes,
The little birds are piping yet
Among the bushes and the trees;
There's a cuckoo, and one or two thrushes,
And a far-off wind that rushes,
And a sound of water that gushes,
And the cuckoo's sovereign cry
Fills all the hollow of the sky.
Who would go "parading"
In London, "and masquerading",
On such a night of June
With that beautiful soft half-moon,
And all these innocent blisses?
On such a night as this is!

On summer nights, William Wordsworth and his sister Dorothy would sit outside after sunset, listening to the birds sing, and watching the moon.

My Heart's in the Highlands
Robert Burns

My heart's in the Highlands, my heart is not here;
My heart's in the Highlands a-chasing the deer;
Chasing the wild deer, and following the roe,
My heart's in the Highlands, wherever I go.

Farewell to the Highlands, farewell to the North,
The birth-place of Valour, the country of Worth;
Wherever I wander, wherever I rove,
The hills of the Highlands for ever I love.

Farewell to the mountains, high cover'd with snow;
Farewell to the straths and green valleys below;
Farewell to the forests and wild-hanging woods;
Farewell to the torrents and loud-pouring floods.

My heart's in the Highlands, my heart is not here;
My heart's in the Highlands a-chasing the deer;
Chasing the wild deer, and following the roe;
My heart's in the Highlands, wherever I go.

When I Was One-and-Twenty
A.E. Housman

When I was one-and-twenty
I heard a wise man say,
"Give crowns and pounds and guineas
But not your heart away;
Give pearls away and rubies
But keep your fancy free."
But I was one-and-twenty,
No use to talk to me.

When I was one-and-twenty
I heard him say again,
"The heart out of the bosom
Was never given in vain;
'Tis paid with sighs a plenty
And sold for endless rue."
And I am two-and-twenty,
And oh, 'tis true, 'tis true.

This is a young man's experience of a first unhappy love affair. Housman suggests that all love will be betrayed.

A Red, Red Rose
Robert Burns

O my Luve's like a red, red rose,
That's newly sprung in June;
O my Luve's like the melodie
That's sweetly play'd in tune.

As fair art thou, my bonie lass,
So deep in luve am I,
And I will luve thee still, my dear,
Till a' the seas gang dry.

Till a' the seas gang dry, my dear,
And the rocks melt wi' the sun:
I will luve thee still, my dear,
While the sands o' life shall run.

And fare thee weel, my only Luve,
And fare thee weel a while!
And I will come again, my Luve,
Tho' it were ten thousand mile!

Like many of his compositions, Burns based this on a traditional folk song he heard on his travels.

Where Go the Boats?
Robert Louis Stevenson

Dark brown is the river,
Golden is the sand.
It flows along for ever,
With trees on either hand.

Green leaves a-floating,
Castles of the foam,
Boats of mine a-boating—
Where will all come home?

On goes the river
And out past the mill,
Away down the valley,
Away down the hill.

Away down the river,
A hundred miles or more,
Other little children
Shall bring my boats ashore.

Henry King
Who Chewed Bits of String, and Was Early Cut Off In Dreadful Agonies

Hilaire Belloc

The Chief Defect of Henry King
Was chewing little bits of String.
At last he swallowed some which tied
Itself in ugly Knots inside.
Physicians of the Utmost Fame
Were called at once; but when they came
They answered, as they took their Fees,
"There is no Cure for this Disease.
Henry will very soon be dead."
His Parents stood about his Bed
Lamenting his Untimely Death,
When Henry, with his Latest Breath,
Cried, "Oh, my Friends, be warned by me,
That Breakfast, Dinner, Lunch, and Tea
Are all the Human Frame requires…"
With that, the Wretched Child expires.

The rhyming makes this poem an easy one to learn.

Sweet and Low
Alfred, Lord Tennyson

Sweet and low, sweet and low,
Wind of the western sea,
Low, low, breathe and blow,
Wind of the western sea!
Over the rolling waters go,
Come from the dying moon, and blow,
Blow him again to me;
While my little one, while my pretty one, sleeps.

Sleep and rest, sleep and rest,
Father will come to thee soon;
Rest, rest, on mother's breast,
Father will come to thee soon;
Father will come to his babe in the nest,
Silver sails all out of the west
Under the silver moon:
Sleep my little one, sleep, my pretty one, sleep.

*This beautiful lullaby is full of Tennyson's exquisite sense of
the sound of words.*

On the Ning Nang Nong
Spike Milligan

On the Ning Nang Nong
Where the Cows go Bong!
And the Monkeys all say Boo!
There's a Nong Nang Ning
Where the trees go Ping!
And the tea pots Jibber Jabber Joo.
On the Nong Ning Nang
All the mice go Clang!
And you just can't catch 'em when they do!
So it's Ning Nang Nong!
Cows go Bong!
Nong Nang Ning!
Trees go Ping!
Nong Ning Nang!
The mice go Clang!

What a noisy place to belong,
Is the Ning Nang Ning Nang Nong!!

This was voted the nation's favourite comic poem in a 1998 BBC poll.

Rat Race
John Agard

Rat Race?
Don't make us laugh.
It's you humans
who're always in a haste.

Ever seen a rat
in a bowler hat
rushing to catch a train?

Ever seen a rat
with a briefcase
hurrying through the rain?

And isn't it a fact
that all that hurry-hurry
gives you humans heart attacks?

No, my friend,
we rats relax.

Pass the cheese,
please.

Why not recite this to your pet rat?

Alligator
Grace Nichols

If you want to see an alligator
you must go down the muddy slushy end
of the old Caroony River.

I know an alligator
who's living down there.
She's a-big. She's a-mean. She's a-wild.
She's a-fierce.

But if you really want to see an alligator
you must go down to the muddy slushy end
of the old Caroony River.

Go down gently to that river and say
"Alligator Mama
Alligator Mama
Alligator Mamaaaaaaaa"

And up she'll rise
but don't stick around
RUN FOR YOUR LIFE.

Scare your mates – act this poem out.

Please Mrs Butler
Allan Ahlberg

Please Mrs Butler
This boy Derek Drew
Keeps copying my work, Miss.
What shall I do?

Go and sit in the hall, dear.
Go and sit in the sink.
Take your books on the roof, my lamb.
Do whatever you think.

Please Mrs Butler
This boy Derek Drew
Keeps taking my rubber, Miss.
What shall I do?

Keep it in your hand, dear.
Hide it up your vest.
Swallow it if you like, my love.
Do what you think best.

Please Mrs Butler
This boy Derek Drew
Keeps calling me rude names, Miss.
What shall I do?

Lock yourself in the cupboard, dear.
Run away to sea.
Do whatever you can, my flower.
But *don't ask me!*

Why don't you see if your teacher can recite this poem?

Eldorado
Edgar Allan Poe

Gaily bedight,
A gallant knight
In sunshine and in shadow,
Had journeyed long,
Singing a song,
In search of Eldorado.

But he grew old –
This knight so bold –
And – o'er his heart a shadow
Fell as he found
No spot of ground
That looked like Eldorado.

And, as his strength
Failed him at length,
He met a pilgrim shadow:
"Shadow," said he,
"Where can it be –
This land of Eldorado?"

"Over the Mountains
Of the Moon,
Down the Valley of the Shadow,
Ride, boldly ride,"
The shade replied,
"If you seek for Eldorado."

*Eldorado is a legendary city of gold somewhere in South
America.*

Three
Carol Ann Duffy

I met a miniature King
by the side of the road,
wearing a crown
and an ermine suit –
important, small,
plump as a natterjack toad.
Kneel! he shrieked, *Kneel for the King!*
Certainly not, I said,
I'll do no such thing.

I saw a Giantess,
tall as a tree.
You'll do for a doll, she bellowed,
just the toy for me!
Into the box! Scream hard! Scream long!
I stared at her mad pond eyes
then skipped away.
Dream on. . .

I bumped into an Invisible Boy – *ouch!* –
at the edge of the field.
Give me a chocolate drop,
said a voice.
What do you say? Said I.
Please.
So I did
then stared as it floated mid-air
and melted away.

These are three of the people I met yesterday.

Carol Ann Duffy likes "to use simple words but in a complicated way".

Buckingham Palace
A.A. Milne

They're changing guard at Buckingham Palace –
Christopher Robin went down with Alice.
Alice is marrying one of the guard.
"A soldier's life is terrible hard,"
　　Says Alice.

They're changing guard at Buckingham Palace –
Christopher Robin went down with Alice.
We saw a guard in a sentry-box.
"One of the sergeants looks after their socks,"
　　Says Alice.

They're changing guard at Buckingham Palace –
Christopher Robin went down with Alice.
We looked for the King, but he never came.
"Well, God take care of him, all the same,"
　　Says Alice.

They're changing guard at Buckingham Palace –
Christopher Robin went down with Alice.
They've great big parties inside the grounds.
"I wouldn't be King for a hundred pounds,"
    Says Alice.

They're changing guard at Buckingham Palace –
Christopher Robin went down with Alice.
A face looked out, but it wasn't the King's.
"He's much too busy a-signing things,"
    Says Alice.

They're changing guard at Buckingham Palace –
Christopher Robin went down with Alice.
"Do you think the King knows all about me?"
"Sure to, dear, but it's time for tea,"
    Says Alice.

Marching makes learning this poem fun.

The Owl and the Pussycat
Edward Lear

I

The Owl and the Pussycat went to sea
In a beautiful pea-green boat,
They took some honey, and plenty of money,
Wrapped up in a five-pound note.
The Owl looked up to the stars above,
And sang to a small guitar,
"O lovely Pussy! O Pussy, my love,
What a beautiful Pussy you are,
You are,
You are!
What a beautiful Pussy you are!"

II

Pussy said to the Owl, "You elegant fowl!
How charmingly sweet you sing!
O let us be married! too long we have tarried:
But what shall we do for a ring?"
They sailed away, for a year and a day,

To the land where the Bong-tree grows
And there in a wood a Piggy-wig stood
With a ring at the end of his nose,
His nose,
His nose,
With a ring at the end of his nose.

III

"Dear Pig, are you willing to sell for one shilling
Your ring?" Said the Piggy, "I will,"
So they took it away, and were married next day
By the Turkey who lives on the hill.
They dined on mince, and slices of quince,
Which they ate with a runcible spoon;
And hand in hand, on the edge of the sand,
They danced by the light of the moon,
The moon,
The moon,
They danced by the light of the moon.

Lear delighted in the sound of words, both real and imaginary.
His nonsense works are full of made-up words.

The King's Breakfast
A.A. Milne

The King asked
The Queen, and
The Queen asked
The Dairymaid:
"Could we have some butter for
The Royal slice of bread?"
The Queen asked
The Dairymaid,
The Dairymaid
Said, "Certainly,
I'll go and tell
The cow
Now
Before she goes to bed."

The Dairymaid
She curtsied,
And went and told
The Alderney:
"Don't forget the butter for
The Royal slice of bread."

The Alderney
Said sleepily:
"You'd better tell
His Majesty
That many people nowadays
Like marmalade
Instead."

The Dairymaid
Said, "Fancy!"
And went to
Her Majesty.
She curtsied to the Queen, and
She turned a little red:
"Excuse me,
Your Majesty,
For taking of
The liberty,
But marmalade is tasty, if
It's very
Thickly
Spread."

The Queen said
"Oh!"
And went to
His Majesty:
"Talking of the butter for

The Royal slice of bread,
Many people
Think that
Marmalade
Is nicer.
Would you like to try a little
Marmalade
Instead?"

The King said,
"Bother!"
And then he said,
"Oh, deary me!"
The King sobbed, "Oh, deary me!"
And went back to bed.
"Nobody,"
He whimpered,
"Could call me
A fussy man;
I *only* want
A little bit
Of butter for
My bread!"

The Queen said:
"There, there!"
And went to
The Dairymaid.

The Dairymaid
Said, "There, there!"
And went to the shed.
The cow said,
"There, there!
I didn't really
Mean it;
Here's milk for his porringer,
And butter for his bread."

The Queen took
The butter
And brought it to
His Majesty;
The King said,
"Butter, eh?"
And bounced out of bed.
"Nobody," he said:
As he kissed her
Tenderly,
"Nobody," he said,
As he slid down
The banisters,
"Nobody,
My darling,
Could call me
A fussy man –

BUT
I do like a little bit of butter to my bread!"

Section 2

Skip

Skip into a slightly more difficult poem!

Eternity
William Blake

He who binds to himself a joy
Does the winged life destroy;
But he who kisses the joy as it flies
Lives in eternity's sun rise.

This is the choice of the Right Honourable Nick Clegg MP who learned it as a child and still loves it today. He writes that "it is a wonderful poem for children, as it is short, simple, and emphasizes the importance of spontaneity, possibility, and the beauty of fully embracing life and seizing the opportunities which come our way".

He Wishes for the Cloths of Heaven
W.B. Yeats

Had I the heavens' embroidered cloths,
Enwrought with golden and silver light,
The blue and the dim and the dark cloths
Of night and light and the half-light,
I would spread the cloths under your feet:
But I, being poor, have only my dreams;
I have spread my dreams under your feet;
Tread softly because you tread on my dreams.

Why don't you see how many of the grown-ups you know recognize the last line of this poem?

"The Isle is full of noises" from The Tempest
William Shakespeare

Be not afeard; the isle is full of noises,
Sounds and sweet airs, that give delight, and hurt not.
Sometimes a thousand twangling instruments
Will hum about mine ears, and sometime voices,
That, if I then had wak'd after long sleep,
Will make me sleep again: and then, in dreaming,
The clouds methought would open, and show riches
Ready to drop upon me; that, when I wak'd,
I cried to dream again.

*Caliban, who makes this speech, is a native of the island
where the magical duke Prospero and his daughter Miranda
are shipwrecked. This extract typifies Shakespeare's lovely
use of language.*

I Had a Dove
John Keats

I had a dove and the sweet dove died;
And I have thought it died of grieving:
O, what could it grieve for? Its feet were tied,
With a silken thread of my own hand's weaving;
Sweet little red feet! why should you die –
Why should you leave me, sweet dove! why?
You liv'd alone on the forest-tree,
Why, pretty thing! could you not live with me?
I kiss'd you oft and gave you white peas;
Why not live sweetly, as in the green trees?

Song On May Morning
John Milton

Now the bright morning star, Day's harbinger,
Comes dancing from the East, and leads with her
The flowery May, who from her green lap throws
The yellow Cowslip, and the pale Primrose.
Hail bounteous May that dost inspire
Mirth, and youth, and warm desire,
Woods and groves, are of thy dressing,
Hill and dale, doth boast thy blessing.
Thus we salute thee with our early song,
And welcome thee, and wish thee long.

A perfect poem for springtime.

Pied Beauty
Gerard Manley Hopkins

Glory be to God for dappled things—
    For skies of couple-colour as a brinded cow;
    For rose-moles all in stipple upon trout that swim;
Fresh-firecoal chestnut-falls; finches' wings;
    Landscape plotted and pieced—fold, fallow, and plough;
    And all trades, their gear and tackle and trim.

All things counter, original, spare, strange;
    Whatever is fickle, freckled (who knows how?)
    With swift, slow; sweet, sour; adazzle, dim;
He fathers-forth whose beauty is past change:
    Praise him.

This poem really comes alive when it's read aloud.

"This scepter'd isle" from Richard II

William Shakespeare

This royal throne of kings, this scepter'd isle,
This earth of majesty, this seat of Mars,
This other Eden, demi-paradise,
This fortress built by Nature for herself
Against infection and the hand of war,
This happy breed of men, this little world,
This precious stone set in the silver sea,
Which serves it in the office of a wall,
Or as a moat defensive to a house,
Against the envy of less happier lands;
This blessed plot, this earth, this realm, this England.

On his death bed, John of Gaunt, uncle to the monarch, reflects on the sorry state of the country under the rule of King Richard II, but in so doing gives a passionate hymn of praise to England.

"Loveliest of trees, the cherry now"
A.E. Housman

Loveliest of trees, the cherry now
Is hung with bloom along the bough,
And stands about the woodland ride
Wearing white for Eastertide.

Now, of my threescore years and ten,
Twenty will not come again,
And take from seventy springs a score,
It only leaves me fifty more.

And since to look at things in bloom
Fifty springs are little room,
About the woodlands I will go
To see the cherry hung with snow.

This is taken from **A Shropshire Lad,** *Housman's nostalgic elegy to rural England.*

When You Are Old
W.B. Yeats

When you are old and grey and full of sleep,
    And nodding by the fire, take down this book,
    And slowly read, and dream of the soft look
Your eyes had once, and of their shadows deep;

How many loved your moments of glad grace,
    And loved your beauty with love false or true,
    But one man loved the pilgrim soul in you,
And loved the sorrows of your changing face;

And bending down beside the glowing bars,
    Murmur, a little sadly, how love fled
    And paced upon the mountains overhead
And hid his face amid a crowd of stars.

We'll Go No More A-Roving
George Gordon, Lord Byron

So, we'll go no more a-roving
   So late into the night,
Though the heart be still as loving,
   And the moon be still as bright.

For the sword outwears its sheath,
   And the soul wears out the breast,
And the heart must pause to breathe,
   And love itself have rest.

Though the night was made for loving,
   And the day returns too soon,
Yet we'll go no more a-roving
   By the light of the moon.

Piano

D.H. Lawrence

Softly, in the dusk, a woman is singing to me;
Taking me back down the vista of years, till I see
A child sitting under the piano, in the boom of the tingling strings
And pressing the small, poised feet of a mother who smiles
    as she sings.

In spite of myself, the insidious mastery of song
Betrays me back, till the heart of me weeps to belong
To the old Sunday evenings at home, with winter outside
And hymns in the cosy parlour, the tinkling piano our guide.

So now it is vain for the singer to burst into clamour
With the great black piano appassionato. The glamour
Of childish days is upon me, my manhood is cast
Down in the flood of remembrance, I weep like a child for the past.

A moving poem about childhood memories.

The Lake Isle of Innisfree
W.B. Yeats

I will arise and go now, and go to Innisfree,
And a small cabin build there, of clay and wattles made:
Nine bean-rows will I have there, a hive for the honey-bee,
     And live alone in the bee-loud glade.

And I shall have some peace there, for peace comes dropping slow,
Dropping from the veils of the morning to where the cricket sings;
There midnight's all a glimmer, and noon a purple glow,
     And evening full of the linnet's wings.

I will arise and go now, for always night and day
I hear lake water lapping with low sounds by the shore;
While I stand on the roadway, or on the pavements grey,
     I hear it in the deep heart's core.

Bright Star
John Keats

Bright star, would I were steadfast as thou art—
Not in lone splendour hung aloft the night
And watching, with eternal lids apart,
Like nature's patient, sleepless Eremite,
The moving waters at their priestlike task
Of pure ablution round earth's human shores,
Or gazing on the new soft fallen mask
Of snow upon the mountains and the moors—
No—yet still steadfast, still unchangeable,
Pillow'd upon my fair love's ripening breast,
To feel for ever its soft fall and swell,
Awake for ever in a sweet unrest,
Still, still to hear her tender-taken breath,
And so live ever—or else swoon to death.

Keats composed this sonnet when he was sailing to Italy, a trip his friends and doctor hoped would cure him of the tuberculosis from which he was suffering. It has been suggested that the poem was addressed to Fanny Brawne, to whom he had recently become engaged.

Leisure
W. H. Davies

What is this life if, full of care,
We have no time to stand and stare.

No time to stand beneath the boughs
And stare as long as sheep or cows.

No time to see, when woods we pass,
Where squirrels hide their nuts in grass:

No time to see, in broad daylight,
Streams full of stars, like skies at night.

No time to turn at Beauty's glance,
And watch her feet, how they can dance.

No time to wait till her mouth can
Enrich that smile her eyes began.

A poor life this if, full of care,
We have no time to stand and stare.

A call to calm down. . .

Shipping Forecast
Seamus Heaney

Dogger, Rockall, Malin, Irish Sea:
Green, swift upsurges, North Atlantic flux
Conjured by that strong gale-warning voice,
Collapse into a sibilant penumbra.
Midnight and closedown. Sirens of the tundra,
Off eel-road, seal-road, keel-road, whale-road, raise
Their wind-compounded keen behind the baize
And drive the trawlers to the lee of Wicklow.
L'Etoile, Le Guillemott, La Belle Hélène
Nursed their bright names this morning in the bay
That toiled like mortar. It was marvellous
And actual, I said out loud, "A haven,"
The word deepening, clearing, like the sky
Elsewhere on Minches, Cromarty, The Faroes.

Enjoy the sounds of these words.

Upon Westminster Bridge
William Wordsworth

Earth has not anything to show more fair:
    Dull would he be of soul who could pass by
    A sight so touching in its majesty:
This City now doth like a garment wear

The beauty of the morning: silent, bare,
    Ships, towers, domes, theatres, and temples lie
    Open unto the fields, and to the sky,
All bright and glittering in the smokeless air.

Never did sun more beautifully steep
    In his first splendour valley, rock, or hill;
Ne'er saw I, never felt, a calm so deep!

The river glideth at his own sweet will:
    Dear God! the very houses seem asleep;
And all that mighty heart is lying still!

Chosen by the writer Ruth Rendell because "it is short. It introduces children to the sonnet form and it is easy to learn. Although it was written two hundred years ago, it is still a true picture of London and there is nothing in it too difficult for quite a small child to understand".

The Soldier
Rupert Brooke

If I should die, think only this of me:
That there's some corner of a foreign field
That is for ever England. There shall be
In that rich earth a richer dust concealed;
A dust whom England bore, shaped, made aware,
Gave, once her flowers to love, her ways to roam,
A body of England's, breathing English air,
Washed by the rivers, blessed by the suns of home.

And think, this heart, all evil shed away,
A pulse in the eternal mind, no less
Gives somewhere back the thoughts by England given;
Her sights and sounds; dreams happy as her day;
And laughter, learnt of friends; and gentleness,
In hearts at peace, under an English heaven.

Rupert Brooke is very famous for the poetry he wrote about the First World War.

"Like Rain it sounded till it curved"
Emily Dickinson

Like Rain it sounded till it curved
And then I knew 'twas Wind—
It walked as wet as any Wave
But swept as dry as sand—
When it had pushed itself away
To some remotest Plain
A coming as of Hosts was heard
That was indeed the Rain—
It filled the Wells, it pleased the Pools
It warbled in the Road—
It pulled the spigot from the Hills
And let the Floods abroad—
It loosened acres, lifted seas
The sites of Centres stirred
Then like Elijah rode away
Upon a Wheel of Cloud.

Recite this next time there is a storm brewing!

The Donkey
G.K. Chesterton

When fishes flew and forests walked
    And figs grew upon thorn,
Some moment when the moon was blood
    Then surely I was born.

With monstrous head and sickening cry
    And ears like errant wings,
The devil's walking parody
    On all four-footed things.

The tattered outlaw of the earth,
    Of ancient crooked will;
Starve, scourge, deride me: I am dumb,
    I keep my secret still.

Fools! For I also had my hour;
    One far fierce hour and sweet:
There was a shout about my ears,
    And palms before my feet.

A poem for Easter.

The Song of the Mischievous Dog
Dylan Thomas

There are many who say that a dog has its day,
And a cat has a number of lives;
There are others who think that a lobster is pink,
And that bees never work in their hives.
There are fewer, of course, who insist that a horse
Has a horn and two humps on its head,
And a fellow who jests that a mare can build nests
Is as rare as a donkey that's red.
Yet in spite of all this, I have moments of bliss,
For I cherish a passion for bones,
And though doubtful of biscuit, I'm willing to risk it,
And I love to chase rabbits and stones.
But my greatest delight is to take a good bite
At a calf that is plump and delicious;
And if I indulge in a bite at a bulge,
Let's hope you won't think me too vicious.

This was Dylan Thomas's first published poem; it appeared in the Swansea Grammar School magazine when he was just eleven.

Break, Break, Break
Alfred, Lord Tennyson

Break, break, break,
   On thy cold grey stones, O Sea!
And I would that my tongue could utter
   The thoughts that arise in me.

O well for the fisherman's boy,
   That he shouts with his sister at play!
O well for the sailor lad,
   That he sings in his boat on the bay!

And the stately ships go on
   To their haven under the hill;
But O for the touch of a vanish'd hand,
   And the sound of a voice that is still!

Break, break, break
   At the foot of thy crags, O Sea!
But the tender grace of a day that is dead
   Will never come back to me.

These moving lines are from a poem called In Memoriam, *which Tennyson wrote when his friend died.*

Stopping By Woods on a Snowy Evening

Robert Frost

Whose woods these are I think I know.
His house is in the village, though;
He will not see me stopping here
To watch his woods fill up with snow.

My little horse must think it queer
To stop without a farmhouse near
Between the woods and frozen lake
The darkest evening of the year.

He gives his harness bells a shake
To ask if there is some mistake.
The only other sound's the sweep
Of easy wind and downy flake.

The woods are lovely, dark and deep.
But I have promises to keep,
And miles to go before I sleep,
And miles to go before I sleep.

Jerusalem
William Blake

And did those feet in ancient time
Walk upon England's mountains green?
And was the holy Lamb of God
On England's pleasant pastures seen?

And did the Countenance Divine
Shine forth upon our clouded hills?
And was Jerusalem builded here
Among these dark Satanic Mills?

Bring me my Bow of burning gold:
Bring me my Arrows of desire:
Bring me my Spear: O clouds unfold!
Bring me my Chariot of fire!

I will not cease from Mental Fight,
Nor shall my Sword sleep in my hand
Till we have built Jerusalem
In England's green and pleasant Land.

You probably know this poem already . . . as a song. It's often sung in England, at sports events, in churches and in schools.

The Splendour Falls
Alfred, Lord Tennyson

The splendour falls on castle walls
And snowy summits old in story:
The long light shakes across the lakes,
And the wild cataract leaps in glory.
Blow, bugle, blow, set the wild echoes flying,
Blow, bugle; answer, echoes, dying, dying, dying.

O hark, O hear! how thin and clear,
And thinner, clearer, farther going!
O sweet and far from cliff and scar
The horns of Elfland faintly blowing!
Blow, let us hear the purple glens replying:
Blow, bugle; answer, echoes, dying, dying, dying.

O love, they die in yon rich sky,
They faint on hill or field or river:
Our echoes roll from soul to soul,
And grow for ever and for ever.
Blow, bugle, blow, set the wild echoes flying,
And answer, echoes, answer, dying, dying, dying.

This is taken from Tennyson's wonderful long narrative poem, **The Princess.**

She Walks In Beauty Like the Night
George Gordon, Lord Byron

She walks in beauty, like the night
    Of cloudless climes and starry skies,
And all that's best of dark and bright
    Meet in her aspect and her eyes,
Thus mellow'd to that tender light
    Which heaven to gaudy day denies.

One shade the more, one ray the less
    Had half impair'd the nameless grace
Which waves in every raven tress
    Or softly lightens o'er her face,
Where thoughts serenely sweet express
    How pure, how dear their dwelling place.

And on that cheek and o'er that brow
    So soft, so calm, yet eloquent,
The smiles that win. The tints that glow,
    But tell of days in goodness spent,
A mind at peace with all below,
    A heart whose love is innocent!

The Night-piece, to Julia
Robert Herrick

Her eyes the glow-worm lend thee;
The shooting stars attend thee;
   And the elves also,
   Whose little eyes glow
Like the sparks of fire, befriend thee.

No will-o'-the-wisp mislight thee;
Nor snake or slow-worm bite thee;
   But on, on thy way,
   Not making a stay,
Since ghost there's none to affright thee.

Let not the dark thee cumber;
What though the moon does slumber?
   The stars of the night
   Will lend thee their light,
Like tapers clear without number.

Then, Julia, let me woo thee,
Thus, thus to come unto me;
   And when I shall meet
   Thy silv'ry feet,
My soul I'll pour into thee.

Jilly Cooper chose this "because my mother introduced me to it when I was about five. I was always terrified of the dark, particularly during the war, with the blackouts, and she made me learn this poem by heart to comfort me. It is also very beautiful and she loved it, but I think she left out the last verse as probably being too erotic".

"When that I was and a little tiny boy" from Twelfth Night

William Shakespeare

When that I was and a little tiny boy,
With hey, ho, the wind and the rain,
A foolish thing was but a toy,
For the rain it raineth every day.

But when I came to man's estate,
With hey, ho, the wind and the rain,
'Gainst knaves and thieves men shut the gate,
For the rain it raineth every day.

But when I came, alas! to wive,
With hey, ho, the wind and the rain,
By swaggering could I never thrive,
For the rain it raineth every day.

But when I came unto my beds,
With hey, ho, the wind and the rain,
With toss-pots still had drunken heads,
For the rain it raineth every day.

A great while ago the world begun,
With hey, ho, the wind and the rain,
But that's all one, our play is done,
And we'll strive to please you every day.

In Shakespeare's play these lines are performed by the court jester, who often used comedy to tell the truth about people in power. This poem is easier to learn if you read it aloud, as it will make the old-fashioned language clearer.

The Road Not Taken
Robert Frost

Two roads diverged in a yellow wood,
And sorry I could not travel both
And be one traveler, long I stood
And looked down one as far as I could
To where it bent in the undergrowth;

Then took the other, as just as fair,
And having perhaps the better claim,
Because it was grassy and wanted wear;
Though as for that, the passing there
Had worn them really about the same.

And both that morning equally lay
In leaves no step had trodden black.
Oh, I kept the first for another day!
Yet knowing how way leads on to way,
I doubted if I should ever come back.

I shall be telling this with a sigh
Somewhere ages and ages hence:
Two roads diverged in a wood, and I—
I took the one less traveled by,
And that has made all the difference.

Home Thoughts, From Abroad
Robert Browning

Oh, to be in England
Now that April's there,
And whoever wakes in England
Sees, some morning, unaware,
That the lowest boughs and the brushwood sheaf
Round the elm-tree bole are in tiny leaf,
While the chaffinch sings on the orchard bough
In England—now!

And after April, when May follows,
And the whitethroat builds, and all the swallows!
Hark, where my blossomed pear-tree in the hedge
Leans to the field and scatters on the clover
Blossoms and dewdrops—at the bent spray's edge—
That's the wise thrush; he sings each song twice over,
Lest you should think he never could recapture
The first fine careless rapture!
And though the fields look rough with hoary dew,
All will be gay when noontide wakes anew
The buttercups, the little children's dower
—Far brighter than this gaudy melon-flower!

Ariel's song, from *The Tempest*
William Shakespeare

Come unto these yellow sands,
And then take hands:
Courtsied when you have and kiss'd
The wild waves whist:
Foot it featly here and there,
And sweet sprites bear
The burthen. Hark, hark.
Bow-wow.
The watch-dogs bark.
Bow-wow.
Hark, hark! I hear
The strain of strutting chanticleer
Cry cock-a-diddle-dow.

Full fathom five thy father lies;
Of his bones are coral made;
Those are pearls that were his eyes:
Nothing of him that doth fade,
But doth suffer a sea-change
Into something rich and strange.
Sea-nymphs hourly ring his knell:
Ding-dong.
Hark! now I hear them, — Ding-dong, bell.

No!

Thomas Hood

No sun–no moon!
No morn–no noon–
No dawn–no dusk–no proper time of day–
No sky–no earthly view–
No distance looking blue–
No road–no street–no "t'other side the way"–
No end to any Row–
No indications where the Crescents go–
No top to any steeple–
No recognitions of familiar people–
No courtesies for showing 'em–
No knowing 'em!–
No travelling at all–no locomotion,
No inkling of the way–no notion–
"No go"–by land or ocean–
No mail–no post–
No news from any foreign coast–
No Park–no Ring–no afternoon gentility–
No company–no nobility–

No warmth, no cheerfulness, no healthful ease,
No comfortable feel in any member–
No shade, no shine, no butterflies, no bees,
No fruits, no flowers, no leaves, no birds–
November!

Next time you're told not to say no, say this!

O Captain! My Captain!
Walt Whitman

O Captain! my Captain! our fearful trip is done,
The ship has weather'd every rack, the prize we sought is won,
The port is near, the bells I hear, the people all exulting,
While follow eyes the steady keel, the vessel grim and daring;
   But O heart! heart! heart!
    O the bleeding drops of red,
     Where on the deck my Captain lies,
      Fallen cold and dead.

O Captain! my Captain! rise up and hear the bells;
Rise up—for you the flag is flung—for you the bugle trills,
For you bouquets and ribbon'd wreaths—for you the shores
   a-crowding,
For you they call, the swaying mass, their eager faces turning;
   Here Captain! dear father!
    This arm beneath your head!
     It is some dream that on the deck,
      You've fallen cold and dead.

My Captain does not answer, his lips are pale and still,
My father does not feel my arm, he has no pulse nor will,
The ship is anchor'd safe and sound, its voyage closed and done,
From fearful trip the victor ship comes in with object won;
 Exult O shores, and ring O bells!
  But I with mournful tread,
   Walk the deck my Captain lies,
    Fallen cold and dead.

Walt Whitman wrote this poem about the assassination of the American President Abraham Lincoln.

Clock-a-Clay
John Clare

In the cowslip pips I lie,
Hidden from the buzzing fly,
While green grass beneath me lies,
Pearled wi' dew like fishes' eyes,
Here I lie, a clock-a-clay,
Waiting for the time of day.

While grassy forest quakes surprise,
And the wild wind sobs and sighs,
My gold home rocks as like to fall,
On its pillar green and tall:
When the pattering rain drives by
Clock-a-clay keeps warm and dry.

Day by day and night by night,
All the week I hide from sight;
In the cowslip pips I lie,
In the rain and dew still warm and dry;
Day and night, and night and day,
Red, black-spotted clock-a-clay.

My home shakes in wind and showers,
Pale green pillar topped with flowers,
Bending at the wild wind's breath,
Till I touch the grass beneath;
Here I live, lone clock-a-clay,
Watching for the time of day.

Lots of poetry is based on local folk songs. Here is an example. Can you write a tune for it?

The Loreley

Heinrich Heine, translated by Louis Untermeyer

I cannot tell why this imagined
Despair has fallen on me;
The ghost of an ancient legend
That will not let me be:

The air is cool, and twilight
Flows down the quiet Rhine;
A mountain alone in the high light
Still holds the lingering shine.

The last peak rosily gleaming
Reveals, enthroned in air,
A maiden, lost in dreaming,
Who combs her golden hair.

Combing her hair with a golden
Comb in her rocky bower,
She sings the tune of an olden
Song that has magic power.

The boatman has heard; it has bound him
In the throes of a strange, wild love;
Blind to the reefs that surround him,
He sees but the vision above.

And lo, hungry waters are springing –
The boat and the boatmen are gone . . .
Then silence. And this, with her singing,
The Loreley has done.

Loreley was a mermaid who would appear sitting on a rock, combing her golden hair, and use her song to lure sailors to their deaths.

St Kevin and the Blackbird
Seamus Heaney

And then there was St Kevin and the blackbird.
The saint is kneeling, arms stretched out, inside
His cell, but the cell is narrow, so

One turned-up palm is out the window, stiff
As a crossbeam, when a blackbird lands
and lays in it and settles down to nest.

Kevin feels the warm eggs, the small breast, the tucked
Neat head and claws and, finding himself linked
Into the network of eternal life,

Is moved to pity: now he must hold his hand
Like a branch out in the sun and rain for weeks
Until the young are hatched and fledged and flown.

And since the whole thing's imagined anyhow,
Imagine being Kevin. Which is he?
Self-forgetful or in agony all the time

From the neck on out down through his hurting forearms?
Are his fingers sleeping? Does he still feel his knees?
Or has the shut-eyed blank of underearth

Crept up through him? Is there distance in his head?
Alone and mirrored clear in love's deep river,
"To labour and not to seek reward," he prays,

A prayer his body makes entirely
For he has forgotten self, forgotten bird
And on the riverbank forgotten the river's name.

Heaney's poem is based on the story of the blackbird that laid her eggs in St Kevin's hand when his arms were outstretched in prayer. The eggs safely hatched!

I wandered lonely as a cloud
William Wordsworth

I wandered lonely as a cloud
    That floats on high o'er vales and hills,
When all at once I saw a crowd,
    A host, of golden daffodils;
Beside the lake, beneath the trees,
Fluttering and dancing in the breeze.

Continuous as the stars that shine
    And twinkle on the milky way,
They stretched in never-ending line
    Along the margin of a bay:
Ten thousand saw I at a glance,
Tossing their heads in sprightly dance.

The waves beside them danced: but they
    Out-did the sparkling waves in glee:
A poet could not but be gay,
    In such a jocund company:
I gazed—and gazed—but little thought
What wealth the show to me had brought:

For oft, when on my couch I lie
    In vacant or in pensive mood,
They flash upon that inward eye
    Which is the bliss of solitude;
And then my heart with pleasure fills
And dances with the daffodils.

This must be the most famous poem about daffodils ever written!

The Way Through the Woods
Rudyard Kipling

They shut the road through the woods
Seventy years ago.
Weather and rain have undone it again,
And now you would never know
There was once a road through the woods
Before they planted the trees.
It is underneath the coppice and heath,
And the thin anemones.
Only the keeper sees
That, where the ring-dove broods,
And the badgers roll at ease,
There was once a road through the woods.

Yet, if you enter the woods
Of a summer evening late,
When the night-air cools on the trout-ringed pools
Where the otter whistles his mate,
(They fear not men in the woods,
Because they see so few)

You will hear the beat of a horse's feet,
And the swish of a skirt in the dew,
Steadily cantering through
The misty solitudes,
As though they perfectly knew
The old lost road through the woods...
But there is no road through the woods.

Rudyard Kipling was also a very famous author. He wrote
The Jungle Book.

The Old Vicarage, Grantchester
Rupert Brooke

Ah God! to see the branches stir
Across the moon at Grantchester!
To smell the thrilling-sweet and rotten
Unforgettable, unforgotten
River-smell, and hear the breeze
Sobbing in the little trees.
Say, do the elm-clumps greatly stand
Still guardians of that holy land?
The chestnuts shade, in reverend dream,
The yet unacademic stream?
Is dawn a secret shy and cold
Anadyomene, silver-gold?
And sunset still a golden sea
From Haslingfield to Madingley?

And after, ere the night is born,
Do hares come out about the corn?
Oh, is the water sweet and cool,
Gentle and brown, above the pool?

And laughs the immortal river still
Under the mill, under the mill?
Say, is there Beauty yet to find?
And Certainty? and Quiet kind?
Deep meadows yet, for to forget
The lies, and truths, and pain? – oh! yet
Stands the Church clock at ten to three?
And is there honey still for tea?

This is taken from a much longer poem about the house in which Rupert Brooke once lived.

Jabberwocky
Lewis Carroll

'Twas brillig, and the slithy toves
    Did gyre and gimble in the wabe;
All mimsy were the borogoves,
    And the mome raths outgrabe.

"Beware the Jabberwock, my son!
    The jaws that bite, the claws that catch!
Beware the Jubjub bird, and shun
    The frumious Bandersnatch!"

He took his vorpal sword in hand:
    Long time the manxome foe he sought—
So rested he by the Tumtum tree,
    And stood awhile in thought.

And as in uffish thought he stood,
    The Jabberwock, with eyes of flame,
Came whiffling through the tulgey wood,
    And burbled as it came!

One, two! One, two! And through and through
    The vorpal blade went snicker-snack!
He left it dead, and with its head
    He went galumphing back.

"And has thou slain the Jabberwock?
    Come to my arms, my beamish boy!
O frabjous day! Callooh! Callay!"
    He chortled in his joy.

'Twas brillig, and the slithy toves
    Did gyre and gimble in the wabe:
All mimsy were the borogoves,
    And the mome raths outgrabe.

This is Stephen Fry's, by his own admission, "crashingly obvious" choice.

The Passionate Shepherd to His Love
Christopher Marlowe

Come live with me and be my Love,
And we will all the pleasures prove
That hills and valleys, dale and field,
And all the craggy mountains yield.

There will we sit upon the rocks
And see the shepherds feed their flocks,
By shallow rivers, to whose falls
Melodious birds sing madrigals.

There will I make thee beds of roses
And a thousand fragrant posies,
A cap of flowers, and a kirtle
Embroider'd all with leaves of myrtle.

A gown made of the finest wool
Which from our pretty lambs we pull,
Fair linèd slippers for the cold,
With buckles of the purest gold.

A belt of straw and ivy buds
With coral clasps and amber studs:
And if these pleasures may thee move,
Come live with me and be my Love.

Thy silver dishes for thy meat
As precious as the gods do eat,
Shall on an ivory table be
Prepared each day for thee and me.

The shepherd swains shall dance and sing
For thy delight each May-morning:
If these delights thy mind may move,
Then live with me and be my Love.

Timothy Winters
Charles Causley

Timothy Winters comes to school
With eyes as wide as a football pool,
Ears like bombs and teeth like splinters:
A blitz of a boy is Timothy Winters.

His belly is white, his neck is dark,
And his hair is an exclamation mark.
His clothes are enough to scare a crow
And through his britches the blue winds blow.

When teacher talks he won't hear a word
And he shoots down dead the arithmetic-bird,
He licks the patterns off his plate
And he's not even heard of the Welfare State.

Timothy Winters has bloody feet
And he lives in a house on Suez Street,
He sleeps in a sack on the kitchen floor
And they say there aren't boys like him any more.

Old man Winters likes his beer
And his missus ran off with a bombardier.
Grandma sits in the grate with a gin
And Timothy's dosed with an aspirin.

The Welfare Worker lies awake
But the law's as tricky as a ten-foot snake,
So Timothy Winters drinks his cup
And slowly goes on growing up.

At Morning Prayers the Master helves
For children less fortunate than ourselves,
And the loudest response in the room is when
Timothy Winters roars "Amen!"

So come one angel, come on ten:
Timothy Winters says "Amen
Amen amen amen amen."
Timothy Winters, Lord.
   Amen!

The late, great Charles Causley is one of the most underrated poets. The emphatic rhyming scheme and the jolly, hymn-like metre is an ironic counterpoint to the tragic fate of Timothy Winters.

I Remember, I Remember
Thomas Hood

I remember, I remember,
The house where I was born,
The little window where the sun
Came peeping in at morn;
He never came a wink too soon,
Nor brought too long a day,
But now, I often wish the night
Had borne my breath away!

I remember, I remember,
The roses, red and white,
The violets, and the lily-cups,
Those flowers made of light!
The lilacs where the robin built,
And where my brother set
The laburnum on his birthday—
The tree is living yet!

I remember, I remember,
Where I was used to swing,
And thought the air must rush as fresh
To swallows on the wing;
My spirit flew in feathers then,
That is so heavy now,
The summer pools could hardly cool
The fever on my brow!

I remember, I remember,
The fir trees dark and high;
I used to think their slender tops
Were close against the sky:
It was a childish ignorance,
But now 'tis little joy
To know I'm farther off from heav'n
Than when I was a boy.

If

Rudyard Kipling

If you can keep your head when all about you
Are losing theirs and blaming it on you;
If you can trust yourself when all men doubt you,
But make allowance for their doubting too;
If you can wait and not be tired by waiting,
Or being lied about, don't deal in lies,
Or being hated, don't give way to hating,
And yet don't look too good, nor talk too wise:
If you can dream – and not make dreams your master;
If you can think – and not make thoughts your aim;
If you can meet with Triumph and Disaster
And treat those two impostors just the same;
If you can bear to hear the truth you've spoken
Twisted by knaves to make a trap for fools,
Or watch the things you gave your life to, broken,
And stoop and build 'em up with worn-out tools:
If you can make one heap of all your winnings
And risk it on one turn of pitch-and-toss,
And lose, and start again at your beginnings

And never breathe a word about your loss;
If you can force your heart and nerve and sinew
To serve your turn long after they are gone,
And so hold on when there is nothing in you
Except the Will which says to them: "Hold on!"
If you can talk with crowds and keep your virtue,
Or walk with Kings – nor lose the common touch,
If neither foes nor loving friends can hurt you,
If all men count with you, but none too much;
If you can fill the unforgiving minute
With sixty seconds' worth of distance run,
Yours is the Earth and everything that's in it,
And – which is more – you'll be a Man, my son!

In 1996, **If** *was officially voted the Nation's Favourite Poem by BBC viewers and listeners.*

Colonel Fazackerley
Charles Causley

Colonel Fazackerley Butterworth-Toast
Bought an old castle complete with a ghost,
But someone or other forgot to declare
To Colonel Fazak that the spectre was there.

On the very first evening, while waiting to dine,
The Colonel was taking a fine sherry wine,
When the ghost, with a furious flash and a flare,
Shot out of the chimney and shivered, "Beware!"

Colonel Fazackerley put down his glass
And said, "My dear fellow, that's really first class!
I just can't conceive how you do it at all.
I imagine you're going to a Fancy Dress Ball?"

At this, the dread ghost made a withering cry.
Said the Colonel (his monocle firm in his eye),
"Now just how you do it I wish I could think.
Do sit down and tell me, and please have a drink."

The ghost in his phosphorous cloak gave a roar
And floated about between ceiling and floor.
He walked through a wall and returned through a pane
And backed up the chimney and came down again.

Said the Colonel, "With laughter I'm feeling quite weak!"
(As trickles of merriment ran down his cheek).
"My house-warming party I hope you won't spurn.
You MUST say you'll come and you'll give us a turn!"

At this, the poor spectre – quite out of his wits –
Proceeded to shake himself almost to bits.
He rattled his chains and he clattered his bones
And he filled the whole castle with mumbles and groans.

But Colonel Fazackerley, just as before,
Was simply delighted and called out, "Encore!"
At which the ghost vanished, his efforts in vain,
And never was seen at the castle again.

"Oh dear, what a pity!" said Colonel Fazak.
"I don't know his name, so I won't call him back."
And then with a smile that was hard to define,
Colonel Fazackerley went in to dine.

Clive, the Fearless Birdman
Pam Ayres

Clive the fearless birdman was convinced that he could fly.
At night he lay in bed and dreamed of soaring through the sky.
Of cruising through the clouds, of winging far out into space.
And he had a leather helmet and a beak stuck on his face.

Clive the fearless birdman had a wife who did not care
For his fly-by-night ambition of cavorting through the air.
With mocking and with ridicule she did her best to kill it,
And cruelly filled his breakfast plate with cuttlefish and millet.

But in his little potting shed he'd built some mighty wings
Out of balsa wood and sticky tape and plasticine and strings.
Up to his neck in feathers which had taken months to pluck
He laboured with his Evo-Stick, he fashioned and he stuck.

He tried it on at last and slowly turned from side to side.
So wonderful it was that Clive the birdman slumped and cried.
So shiny were the feathers all in silver and in black,
With eiderdown all up the front and turkey down the back.

It strapped on with a harness buckled round his arms and throat,
All made adjustable to fit the thickness of his coat.
Just to see him walking in the street made women shriek
As he flapped by in his harness and his helmet and his beak.

So Clive announced to all the culmination of his search
And told the local papers he'd be jumping off the church.
Seth, the old gravedigger, with his face as black as coal
Said, "If he jumps off the steeple I shan't have to dig a hole!"

And so the day arrived and all the people came to stare,
Police held back the crowds and all the local press was there.
Clive read out a noble speech, an address to the people
That nobody could hear, for it was windy up the steeple.

He stepped out in the sky and flapped his wings just for a minute,
Far above the Vicar's garden as he plummeted straight in it.
He lay there in the cabbages without another flutter
And the beak came off his helmet and went rolling in the gutter.

But far away in Heaven Clive the Birdman reigns supreme
Soaring through the air without the aid of jet or steam,
So at the Pearly Gates if it's with Clive you wish to speak,
You can tell him by his harness and his helmet and his beak.

Let your imagination soar!

The Highwayman
Alfred Noyes

I

The wind was a torrent of darkness among the gusty trees,
The moon was a ghostly galleon tossed upon cloudy seas,
The road was a ribbon of moonlight over the purple moor,
And the highwayman came riding—
Riding—riding—
The highwayman came riding, up to the old inn-door.

II

He'd a French cocked-hat on his forehead, a bunch of lace
    at his chin,
A coat of the claret velvet, and breeches of brown doe-skin;
They fitted with never a wrinkle: his boots were up to the thigh!
And he rode with a jewelled twinkle,
His pistol butts a-twinkle,
His rapier hilt a-twinkle, under the jewelled sky.

III

Over the cobbles he clattered and clashed in the dark inn-yard,
And he tapped with his whip on the shutters, but all was
  locked and barred;
He whistled a tune to the window, and who should be
  waiting there
But the landlord's black-eyed daughter,
Bess, the landlord's daughter,
Plaiting a dark red love-knot into her long black hair.

IV

And dark in the dark old inn-yard a stable-wicket creaked
Where Tim the ostler listened; his face was white and peaked;
His eyes were hollows of madness, his hair like mouldy hay,
But he loved the landlord's daughter,
The landlord's red-lipped daughter,
Dumb as a dog he listened, and he heard the robber say—

V

"One kiss, my bonny sweetheart, I'm after a prize to-night,
But I shall be back with the yellow gold before the morning light;
Yet, if they press me sharply, and harry me through the day,
Then look for me by moonlight,
Watch for me by moonlight,
I'll come to thee by moonlight, though Hell should bar the way."

VI

He rose upright in the stirrups; he scarce could reach her hand,
But she loosened her hair i' the casement! His face burnt like
   a brand
As the black cascade of perfume came tumbling over his breast;
And he kissed its waves in the moonlight,
(Oh, sweet black waves in the moonlight!)
Then he tugged at his rein in the moonlight, and galloped
   away to the west.

A wonderful rhythmic poem that echoes the sound of a horse's hooves.

Ithaka

C. P. Cavafy

translated by Edmund Keeley and Philip Sherrard

As you set out for Ithaka
hope the voyage is a long one,
full of adventure, full of discovery.
Laistrygonians and Cyclops,
angry Poseidon—don't be afraid of them:
you'll never find things like that on your way
as long as you keep your thoughts raised high,
as long as a rare excitement
stirs your spirit and your body.
Laistrygonians and Cyclops,
wild Poseidon—you won't encounter them
unless you bring them along inside your soul,
unless your soul sets them up in front of you.

Hope the voyage is a long one.
May there be many a summer morning when,
with what pleasure, what joy,
you come into harbors seen for the first time;
may you stop at Phoenician trading stations
to buy fine things,

mother of pearl and coral, amber and ebony,
sensual perfume of every kind—
as many sensual perfumes as you can;
and may you visit many Egyptian cities
to gather stores of knowledge from their scholars.

Keep Ithaka always in your mind.
Arriving there is what you are destined for.
But do not hurry the journey at all.
Better if it lasts for years,
so you are old by the time you reach the island,
wealthy with all you have gained on the way,
not expecting Ithaka to make you rich.

Ithaka gave you the marvellous journey.
Without her you would not have set out.
She has nothing left to give you now.

And if you find her poor, Ithaka won't have fooled you.
Wise as you will have become, so full of experience,
you will have understood by then what these Ithakas mean.

In the Greek Myth, Ithaka is the island that Odysseus took ten years to reach after the Trojan war. The story of that journey is **The Odyssey.** *Cavafy's message in the poem is that the point of life is not simply to reach a destination but to enjoy the journey.*

Talking Turkeys
Benjamin Zephaniah

Be nice to yu turkeys dis christmas
Cos turkeys just wanna hav fun
Turkeys are cool, turkeys are wicked
An every turkey has a Mum.
Be nice to yu turkeys dis christmas,
Don't eat it, keep it alive,
It could be yu mate an not on yu plate
Say, Yo! Turkey I'm on your side.

I got lots of friends who are turkeys
An all of dem fear christmas time,
Dey wanna enjoy it, dey say humans destroyed it
An humans are out of dere mind,
Yeah, I got lots of friends who are turkeys
Dey all hav a right to a life,
Not to be caged up an genetically made up
By any farmer an his wife.

Turkeys just wanna play reggae
Turkeys just wanna hip-hop
Can yu imagine a nice young turkey saying,

"I cannot wait for de chop"?
Turkeys like getting presents, dey wanna watch christmas TV,
Turkeys hav brains an turkeys feel pain
In many ways like yu an me.

I once knew a turkey called . . . Turkey
He said "Benji explain to me please,
Who put de turkey in christmas
An what happens to christmas trees?",
I said "I am not too sure turkey
But it's nothing to do wid Christ Mass
Humans get greedy an waste more dan need be
An business men mek loadsa cash".

Be nice to yu turkey dis christmas
Invite dem indoors fe sum greens
Let dem eat cake an let dem partake
In a plate of organic grown beans,
Be nice to yu turkey dis christmas
An spare dem de cut of de knife,
Join Turkeys United an dey'll be delighted
An yu will mek new friends "FOR LIFE".

One for vegetarians to recite at Christmas (and all year round)!

A Man's a Man for a' That
Robert Burns

Is there, for honest Poverty
That hings his head, and a' that;
The coward-slave we pass him by,
We dare be poor for a' that!
For a' that, and a' that.
Our toils obscure an' a' that,
The rank is but the guinea's stamp,
The Man's the gowd for a' that.

What though on hamely fare we dine,
Wear hoddin grey, an' a that;
Gie fools their silks, and knaves their wine;
A Man's a Man for a' that:
For a' that, and a' that,
Their tinsel show, an' a' that;
The honest man, tho' e'er sae poor,
Is king o' men for a' that.

Ye see yon birkie, ca'd a lord,
Wha struts, and stares, and a' that;
Though hundreds worship at his word,
He's but a coof for a' that:

For a' that, an' a' that,
His ribband, star, an' a' that:
The man o' independent mind
He looks an' laughs at a' that –

A prince can mak a belted knight,
A marquis, duke, an' a' that;
But an honest man's aboon his might,
Gude faith he mauna fa' that!
For a' that, an' a' that,
Their dignities an' a' that;
The pith o' Sense, and pride o' Worth,
Are higher rank than a' that.

Then let us pray that come it may,
As come it will for a' that,
That Sense and Worth, o'er a' the earth,
Shall bear the gree, an' a' that.
For a' that, an' a' that,
It's coming yet for a' that,
That Man to Man the warld o'er,
Shall brothers be for a' that.

The author Alexander McCall Smith writes "this is a very moving poem about equality. I remember reading this when I was a young boy and being very struck by it. Burns speak to all ages, to children as well as adults, and the force of what he has to say has not diminished in the slightest".

Casabianca
Felicia Hemans

The boy stood on the burning deck
    Whence all but he had fled;
The flame that lit the battle's wreck
    Shone round him o'er the dead.

Yet beautiful and bright he stood,
    As born to rule the storm;
A creature of heroic blood,
    A proud, though child-like form.

The flames rolled on—he would not go
    Without his Father's word;
That father, faint in death below,
    His voice no longer heard.

He called aloud, "say, Father, say
    If yet my task is done?"
He knew not that the chieftain lay
    Unconscious of his son.

"Speak, father!" once again he cried,
    "If I may yet be gone!"
And but the booming shots replied,
    And fast the flames rolled on.

Upon his brow he felt their breath,
    And in his waving hair,
And looked from that lone post of death
    In still yet brave despair.

And shouted but once more aloud,
    "My father! must I stay?"
While o'er him fast, through sail and shroud,
    The wreathing fires made way.

They wrapt the ship in splendour wild,
    They caught the flag on high,
And streamed above the gallant child,
    Like banners in the sky.

There came a burst of thunder sound—
    The boy—oh! where was he?
Ask of the winds that far around
    With fragments strewed the sea!—

With mast, and helm, and pennon fair,
    That well had borne their part—
But the noblest thing which perished there
    Was that young faithful heart.

*This poem is based on a real event. At the battle of the Nile,
in 1798, the young son of Louis de Casabianca, commander
of the French ship L'Orient, refused to leave his post. He died
when the ship's magazine caught fire.*

Macavity: The Mystery Cat
T.S. ELIOT

Macavity's a Mystery Cat: he's called the Hidden Paw—
For he's the master criminal who can defy the Law.
He's the bafflement of Scotland Yard, the Flying Squad's despair:
For when they reach the scene of crime—*Macavity's not there!*

Macavity, Macavity, there's no one like Macavity,
He's broken every human law, he breaks the law of gravity.
His powers of levitation would make a fakir stare,
And when you reach the scene of crime—*Macavity's not there!*
You may seek him in the basement, you may look up in the air—
But I tell you once and once again, *Macavity's not there!*

Macavity's a ginger cat, he's very tall and thin;
You would know him if you saw him, for his eyes are sunken in.
His brow is deeply lined with thought, his head is highly domed;
His coat is dusty from neglect, his whiskers are uncombed.
He sways his head from side to side, with movements like a snake;
And when you think he's half asleep, he's always wide awake.

Macavity, Macavity, there's no one like Macavity,
For he's a fiend in feline shape, a monster of depravity.
You may meet him in a by-street, you may see him in the square—
But when a crime's discovered, then *Macavity's not there!*

He's outwardly respectable. (They say he cheats at cards.)
And his footprints are not found in any file of Scotland Yard's.
And when the larder's looted, or the jewel-case is rifled,
Or when the milk is missing, or another Peke's been stifled,
Or the greenhouse glass is broken, and the trellis past repair—
Ay, there's the wonder of the thing! *Macavity's not there!*

And when the Foreign Office finds a Treaty's gone astray,
Or the Admiralty lose some plans and drawings by the way,
There may be a scrap of paper in the hall or on the stair—
But it's useless of investigate—*Macavity's not there!*
And when the loss has been disclosed, the Secret Service say:
"It *must* have been Macavity!"—but he's a mile away.
You'll be sure to find him resting, or a-licking of his thumbs,
Or engaged in doing complicated long division sums.

Macavity, Macavity, there's no one like Macavity,
There never was a Cat of such deceitfulness and suavity.
He always has an alibi, or one or two to spare:
And whatever time the deed took place—MACAVITY
     WASN'T THERE!
And they say that all the Cats whose wicked deeds are
     widely known
(I might mention Mungojerrie, I might mention Griddlebone)
Are nothing more than agents for the Cat who all the time
Just controls their operations: the Napoleon of Crime!

This poem is taken from T.S. Eliot's hugely popular collection
Old Possum's Book of Practical Cats. *Possum was Eliot's*
nickname.

The Charge of the Light Brigade
Alfred, Lord Tennyson

Half a league, half a league,
Half a league onward,
All in the valley of Death
Rode the six hundred.
"Forward, the Light Brigade!
Charge for the guns!" he said;
Into the valley of Death
Rode the six hundred.

"Forward, the Light Brigade!"
Was there a man dismay'd ?
Not tho' the soldier knew
Some one had blunder'd:
Theirs not to make reply,
Theirs not to reason why,
Theirs but to do and die:
Into the valley of Death
Rode the six hundred.

Cannon to right of them,
Cannon to left of them,
Cannon in front of them
Volley'd and thunder'd;
Storm'd at with shot and shell,
Boldly they rode and well,
Into the jaws of Death,
Into the mouth of Hell
Rode the six hundred.

Flash'd all their sabres bare,
Flash'd as they turn'd in air,
Sabring the gunners there,
Charging an army, while
All the world wonder'd:
Plunged in the battery-smoke
Right thro' the line they broke;
Cossack and Russian
Reel'd from the sabre-stroke
Shatter'd and sunder'd.
Then they rode back, but not,
Not the six hundred.

Cannon to right of them,
Cannon to left of them,
Cannon behind them
Volley'd and thunder'd;
Storm'd at with shot and shell,

While horse and hero fell,
They that had fought so well
Came thro' the jaws of Death,
Back from the mouth of Hell,
All that was left of them,
Left of six hundred.

When can their glory fade?
O the wild charge they made!
All the world wonder'd.
Honour the charge they made!
Honour the Light Brigade,
Noble six hundred!

Tennyson's poem recalls the disastrous charge of British cavalry led by Lord Cardigan against Russian forces during the Battle of Balaclava, in the Crimean War. Why don't you try acting out the battle whilst learning the poem.

Old Deuteronomy
T.S. Eliot

Old Deuteronomy's lived a long time;
He's a Cat who has lived many lives in succession.
He was famous in proverb and famous in rhyme
A long while before Queen Victoria's accession.
Old Deuteronomy's buried nine wives
And more – I am tempted to say, ninety-nine;
And his numerous progeny prospers and thrives
And the village is proud of him in his decline.
At the sight of that placid and bland physiognomy,
When he sits in the sun on the vicarage wall,
The Oldest Inhabitant croaks: "Well, of all. . .
Things. . . Can it be . . . really! . . . No! . . . Yes! . . .
Ho! hi!
Oh, my eye!
My sight may be failing, but yet I confess
I believe it is Old Deuteronomy!"

Old Deuteronomy sits in the street,
He sits in the High Street on market day;
The bullocks may bellow, the sheep they may bleat,
But the dogs and the herdsmen will turn them away.
The cars and the lorries run over the kerb,
And the villagers put up a notice: ROAD CLOSED –

So that nothing untoward may chance to disturb
Deuteronomy's rest when he feels so disposed
Or when he's engaged in domestic economy:
And the Oldest Inhabitant croaks: "Well, of all . . .
Things . . . Can it be . . . really! . . . No! . . . Yes! . . .
Ho! hi!
Oh, my eye!
I'm deaf of an ear now, but yet I can guess
That the cause of the trouble is Old Deuteronomy!"

Old Deuteronomy lies on the floor
Of the Fox and French Horn for his afternoon sleep;
And when the men say: "There's just time for one more,"
then the landlady from her back parlour will peep
And say: "Now then, out you go, by the back door,
For Old Deuteronomy mustn't be woken –
I'll have the police if there's any uproar" –
And out they all shuffle, without a word spoken.
The digestive repose of that feline's gastronomy
Must never be broken, whatever befall:
And the Oldest Inhabitant croaks: "Well of all . . .
Things . . . Can it be . . . really! . . . Yes! . . . No! . . .
Ho! hi!
Oh, my eye!
My legs may be tottery, I must go slow
And be careful of Old Deuteronomy!"

Chosen by the writer Dick King-Smith "because it makes me laugh, as do all the poems in Old Possum's Book of Practical Cats".

Lochinvar
Sir Walter Scott

O, young Lochinvar is come out of the west,
Through all the wide Border his steed was the best;
And save his good broadsword he weapons had none,
He rode all unarm'd, and he rode all alone.
So faithful in love, and so dauntless in war,
There never was knight like the young Lochinvar.

He stayed not for brake, and he stopp'd not for stone,
He swam the Eske river where ford there was none;
But ere he alighted at Netherby gate,
The bride had consented, the gallant came late:
For a laggard in love, and a dastard in war,
Was to wed the fair Ellen of brave Lochinvar.

So boldly he enter'd the Netherby Hall,
Among bridesmen, and kinsmen, and brothers, and all:
Then spoke the bride's father, his hand on his sword—
(For the poor craven bridegroom said never a word—)
"O come ye in peace here, or come ye in war,
Or to dance at our bridal, young Lord Lochinvar?"—

"I long woo'd your daughter, my suit you denied;—
Love swells like the Solway, but ebbs like its tide—
And now I am come, with this lost love of mine,
To lead but one measure, drink one cup of wine.
There are maidens in Scotland more lovely by far,
That would gladly be bride to the young Lochinvar."

The bride kiss'd the goblet: the knight took it up,
He quaff'd off the wine, and he threw down the cup.
She look'd down to blush, and she look'd up to sigh,
With a smile on her lips, and a tear in her eye.
He took her soft hand, ere her mother could bar—
"Now tread we a measure!" said young Lochinvar.

So stately his form, and so lovely her face,
That never a hall such a galliard did grace;
While her mother did fret, and her father did fume
And the bridegroom stood dangling his bonnet and plume,
And the bride-maidens whisper'd, "'Twere better by far,
To have match'd our fair cousin with young Lochinvar."

One touch to her hand, and one word in her ear,
When they reach'd the hall-door, and the charger stood near;
So light to the croupe the fair lady he swung,
So light to the saddle before her he sprung!
"She is won! we are gone, over bank, bush, and scaur;
They'll have fleet steeds that follow," quoth young Lochinvar.

There was mounting 'mong Graemes of the Netherby clan;
Forsters, Fenwicks, and Musgraves, they rode and they ran:
There was racing and chasing on Cannobie Lee,
But the lost bride of Netherby ne'er did they see.
So daring in love, and so dauntless in war,
Have ye e'er heard of gallant like young Lochinvar?

This is an extract from Sir Walter Scott's epic poem **Marmion,** *published in 1808. It is about the sixteenth-century battle of Flodden Field, at which an invading Scots army suffered a bloody defeat at the hands of the English.*

The Diplomatic Platypus
Patrick Barrington

I had a duck-billed platypus when I was up at Trinity,
With whom I soon discovered a remarkable affinity.
He used to live in lodgings with myself and Arthur Purvis,
And we all went up together for the Diplomatic Service.
I had a certain confidence, I own, in his ability,
He mastered all the subjects with remarkable facility;
And Purvis, though more dubious, agreed that he was clever,
But no one else imagined he had any chance whatever.

I failed to pass the interview, the Board with wry grimaces
Took exception to my boots and then objected to my braces,
And Purvis too was failed by an intolerant examiner
Who said he had his doubts as to his sock-suspenders' stamina.
The bitterness of failure was considerably mollified,
However, by the ease with which our platypus had qualified.

The wisdom of the choice, it soon appeared, was undeniable;
There never was a diplomat more thoroughly reliable.
He never made rash statements his enemies might hold him to,
He never stated anything, for no one ever told him to,
And soon he was appointed, so correct was his behaviour,
Our Minister (without Portfolio) to Trans-Moravia.

My friend was loved and honoured from the Andes to Esthonia,
He soon achieved a pact between Peru and Patagonia,
He never vexed the Russians nor offended the Rumanians,
He pacified the Letts and yet appeased the Lithuanians,
Won approval from his masters down in Downing Street so
    wholly, O,
He was soon to be rewarded with the grant of a Portfolio,
When on the Anniversary of Greek Emancipation,
Alas! He laid an egg in the Bulgarian Legation.

This untoward occurrence caused unheard-of repercussions,
Giving rise to epidemics of sword-clanking in the Prussians.
The Poles began to threaten, and the Finns began to flap at him,
Directing all the blame for this unfortunate mishap at him;
While the Swedes withdrew entirely from the Anglo-Saxon
    dailies
The right of photographing the Aurora Borealis,
And, all efforts at rapprochement in the meantime proving
    barren,
The Japanese in self-defence annexed the Isle of Arran.

My platypus, once thought to be more cautious and more
    tentative
Than any other living diplomatic representative,
Was now a sort of warning to all diplomatic students
Of the risks attached to negligence, the perils of imprudence,
And, branded in the Honours List as 'Platypus, Dame Vera',
Retired, a lonely figure, to lay eggs in Bordighera.

*This poem looks very long, but break it into shorter sections
and it's a lot easier to learn.*

La Belle Dame Sans Merci
John Keats

I.

O what can ail thee, knight-at-arms,
    Alone and palely loitering?
The sedge has withered from the lake,
    And no birds sing.

II.

O what can ail thee, knight-at-arms,
    So haggard and so woe-begone?
The squirrel's granary is full,
    And the harvest's done.

III.

I see a lily on thy brow
    With anguish moist and fever-dew,
And on thy cheeks a fading rose
    Fast withereth too.

IV.

I met a lady in the meads,
    Full beautiful – a faery's child,
Her hair was long, her foot was light,
    And her eyes were wild.

V.

I made a garland for her head,
    And bracelets too, and fragrant zone;
She looked at me as she did love,
    And made sweet moan.

VI.

I set her on my pacing steed,
    And nothing else saw all day long,
For sidelong would she bend, and sing
    A faery's song.

VII.

She found me roots of relish sweet,
    And honey wild, and manna-dew,
And sure in language strange she said –
    "I love thee true".

VIII.

She took me to her elfin grot,
    And there she wept, and sighed full sore,
And there I shut her wild, wild eyes
    With kisses four.

IX.
And there she lullèd me asleep,
    And there I dreamed – ah! woe betide! –
The latest dream I ever dreamt
    On the cold hill's side.

X.
I saw pale kings and princes too,
    Pale warriors, death-pale were they all;
They cried – "La Belle Dame sans Merci
    Hath thee in thrall!"

XI.
I saw their starved lips in the gloam,
    With horrid warning gapèd wide,
And I awoke and found me here,
    On the cold hill's side.

XII.
And this is why I sojourn here,
    Alone and palely loitering,
Though the sedge is withered from the lake,
    And no birds sing.

The French title means "the beautiful lady without pity". Challenge an adult! They're bound to know some of this famous poem already.

The Pobble Who Has No Toes
Edward Lear

I

The Pobble who has no toes
Had once as many as we;
When they said, "Some day you may lose them all";
He replied, "Fish, fiddle-de-dee!"
And his Aunt Jobiska made him drink,
Lavender water tinged with pink,
For she said, "The World in general knows
There's nothing so good for a Pobble's toes!"

II

The Pobble who has no toes,
Swam across the Bristol Channel;
But before he set out he wrapped his nose,
In a piece of scarlet flannel.
For his Aunt Jobiska said, "No harm
Can come to his toes if his nose is warm;
And it's perfectly known that a Pobble's toes
Are safe – provided he minds his nose."

III

The Pobble swam fast and well,
And when boats or ships came near him
He tinkledy-blinkledy-winkled a bell,
So that all the world could hear him.
And all the Sailors and Admirals cried,
When they saw him nearing the further side –
"He has gone to fish, for his Aunt Jobiska's
Runcible Cat with crimson whiskers!"

IV

But before he touched the shore,
The shore of the Bristol Channel,
A sea-green Porpoise carried away
His wrapper of scarlet flannel.
And when he came to observe his feet,
Formerly garnished with toes so neat,
His face at once became forlorn,
On perceiving that all his toes were gone!

V

And nobody ever knew,
From that dark day to the present,
Whoso had taken the Pobble's toes,
In a manner so far from pleasant.
Whether the shrimps or crawfish grey,
Or crafty Mermaids stole them away –
Nobody knew; and nobody knows
How the Pobble was robbed of his twice five toes!

VI

The Pobble who has no toes
Was placed in a friendly Bark,
And they rowed him back, and carried him up,
To his Aunt Jobiska's Park.
And she made him a feast at his earnest wish
Of eggs and buttercups fried with fish;
And she said, "It's a fact the whole world knows,
That Pobbles are happier without their toes."

Matilda
Who Told Lies,
And Was Burned to Death

Hilaire Belloc

Matilda told such Dreadful Lies,
It made one Gasp and Stretch one's Eyes;
Her Aunt, who, from her Earliest Youth,
Had kept a Strict Regard for Truth,
Attempted to Believe Matilda:
The effort very nearly killed her,
And would have done so, had not She
Discovered this Infirmity.
For once, towards the Close of Day,
Matilda, growing tired of play,
And finding she was left alone,
Went tiptoe to the Telephone
And summoned the Immediate Aid
Of London's Noble Fire-Brigade.
Within an hour the Gallant Band
Were pouring in on every hand,
From Putney, Hackney Downs, and Bow
With Courage high and Hearts a-glow
They galloped, roaring through the Town,
"Matilda's House is Burning Down!"
Inspired by British Cheers and Loud
Proceeding from the Frenzied Crowd,
They ran their ladders through a score

Of windows on the Ball Room Floor;
And took Peculiar Pains to Souse
The Pictures up and down the House,
Until Matilda's Aunt succeeded
In showing them they were not needed;
And even then she had to pay
To get the Men to go away!

. . .

It happened that a few Weeks later
Her Aunt was off to the Theatre
To see that Interesting Play
The Second Mrs Tanqueray.
She had refused to take her Niece
To hear this Entertaining Piece:
A Deprivation Just and Wise
To Punish her for Telling Lies.
That Night a Fire *did* break out –
You should have heard Matilda Shout!
You should have heard her Scream and Bawl,
And throw the window up and call
To People passing in the Street –
(The rapidly increasing Heat
Encouraging her to obtain
Their confidence)– but all in vain!
For every time She shouted "Fire!"
They only answered "Little Liar!"
And therefore when her Aunt returned,
Matilda, and the House, were Burned.

*Don't lie about learning this poem . . . you might come to a
sticky end!*

The Pig
Roald Dahl

In England once there lived a big
And wonderfully clever pig.
To everybody it was plain
That Piggy had a massive brain.
He worked out sums inside his head,
There was no book he hadn't read,
He knew what made an airplane fly,
He knew how engines worked and why.
He knew all this, but in the end
One question drove him round the bend:
He simply couldn't puzzle out
What LIFE was really all about.
What was the reason for his birth?
Why was he placed upon this earth?
His giant brain went round and round.
Alas, no answer could be found,
Till suddenly one wondrous night,
All in a flash, he saw the light.
He jumped up like a ballet dancer
And yelled, "By gum, I've got the answer!
They want my bacon, slice by slice,
To sell at a tremendous price!
They want my tender juicy chops
To put in all the butchers' shops!

They want my pork to make a roast
And that's the part'll cost the most!
They want my sausages in strings!
They even want my chitterlings!
The butcher's shop! The carving knife!
That is the reason for my life!"
Such thoughts as these are not designed
To give a pig great peace of mind.

Next morning, in comes Farmer Bland,
A pail of pigswill in his hand,
And Piggy, with a mighty roar,
Bashes the farmer to the floor...
Now comes the rather grisly bit
So let's not make too much of it,
Except that you *must* understand
That Piggy *did eat* Farmer Bland,
He ate him up from head to toe,
Chewing the pieces nice and slow.
It took an hour to reach the feet,
Because there was so much to eat,
And when he'd finished, Pig, of course,
Felt absolutely no remorse.
Slowly he scratched his brainy head
And with a little smile, he said,
"I had a fairly powerful hunch
That he might have me for his lunch.
And so, because I feared the worst,
I thought I'd better eat *him* first."

Perfect with pork chops!

The Song of Hiawatha
Henry Wadsworth Longfellow

By the shores of Gitche Gumee,
By the shining Big-Sea-Water,
Stood the wigwam of Nokomis,
Daughter of the Moon, Nokomis.
Dark behind it rose the forest,
Rose the black and gloomy pine-trees,
Rose the firs with cones upon them;
Bright before it beat the water,
Beat the clear and sunny water,
Beat the shining Big-Sea-Water.

There the wrinkled old Nokomis
Nursed the little Hiawatha,
Rocked him in his linden cradle,
Bedded soft in moss and rushes,
Safely bound with reindeer sinews;
Stilled his fretful wail by saying,
"Hush! the Naked Bear will hear thee!"
Lulled him into slumber, singing,
"Ewa-yea! my little owlet!
Who is this, that lights the wigwam?
With his great eyes lights the wigwam?
Ewa-yea! my little owlet!"

Many things Nokomis taught him
Of the stars that shine in heaven;
Showed him Ishkoodah, the comet,
Ishkoodah, with fiery tresses;
Showed the Death-Dance of the spirits,
Warriors with their plumes and war-clubs,
Flaring far away to northward
In the frosty nights of Winter;
Showed the broad white road in heaven,
Pathway of the ghosts, the shadows,
Running straight across the heavens,
Crowded with the ghosts, the shadows.

At the door on summer evenings
Sat the little Hiawatha;
Heard the whispering of the pine-trees,
Heard the lapping of the waters,
Sounds of music, words of wonder;
'Minne-wawa!' said the Pine-trees,
'Mudway-aushka!' said the water.

Saw the fire-fly, Wah-wah-taysee,
Flitting through the dusk of evening,
With the twinkle of its candle
Lighting up the brakes and bushes;

And he sang the song of children,
Sang the song Nokomis taught him:
"Wah-wah-taysee, little fire-fly,
Little, flitting, white-fire insect,
Little, dancing, white-fire creature,
Light me with your little candle,
Ere upon my bed I lay me,
Ere in sleep I close my eyelids!"

These lines are from Longfellow's epic poem, which was based on the legends of the Ojibwa Indians. This is a great poem for reciting with the whole class.

Little Red Riding Hood and the Wolf
Roald Dahl

As soon as Wolf began to feel
That he would like a decent meal,
He went and knocked on Grandma's door.
When Grandma opened it, she saw
The sharp white teeth, the horrid grin,
And Wolfie said, "May I come in?"
Poor Grandmamma was terrified,
"He's going to eat me up!" she cried.
And she was absolutely right.
He ate her up in one big bite.
But Grandmamma was small and tough,
And Wolfie wailed, "That's not enough!
I haven't yet begun to feel
That I have had a decent meal!"
He ran around the kitchen yelping,
"I've got to have a second helping!"
Then added with a frightful leer,
"I'm therefore going to wait right here
Till Little Miss Red Riding Hood
Comes home from walking in the wood."
He quickly put on Grandma's clothes
(Of course he hadn't eaten those).
He dressed himself in coat and hat.
He put on shoes and after that

He even brushed and curled his hair,
Then sat himself in Grandma's chair.
In came the little girl in red.
She stopped. She stared. And then she said,

"*What great big ears you have, Grandma.*"
"*All the better to hear you with,*" the Wolf replied.
"*What great big eyes you have, Grandma.*"
Said Little Red Riding Hood.
"*All the better to see you with,*" the Wolf replied.

He sat there watching her and smiled.
He thought, I'm going to eat this child.
Compared with her old Grandmamma
She's going to taste like caviar.
Then Little Red Riding Hood said, "*But Grandma,
what a lovely great big furry coat you have on.*"

"That's wrong!" cried Wolf. "Have you forgot
To tell me what BIG TEETH I've got?
Ah well, no matter what you say,
I'm going to eat you anyway."
The small girl smiles. One eyelid flickers.
She whips a pistol from her knickers.
She aims it at the creature's head
And *bang bang bang*, she shoots him dead.
A few weeks later, in the wood,
I came across Miss Riding Hood.
But what a change! No cloak of red,
No silly hood upon her head.
She said, "Hello, and do please note
My lovely furry WOLFSKIN COAT."

*Have you tried writing a poem about a fairytale? Roald Dahl
did it brilliantly.*

Jim
Who Ran Away From His Nurse
and Was Eaten by a Lion
Hilaire Belloc

There was a Boy whose name was Jim;
His Friends were very good to him.
They gave him Tea, and Cakes, and Jam,
And slices of delicious Ham,
And Chocolate with pink inside
And little Tricycles to ride,
And read him Stories through and through,
And even took him to the Zoo—
But there it was the dreadful Fate
Befell him, which I now relate.

You know—or at least you ought to know,
For I have often told you so—
That Children never are allowed
To leave their Nurses in a Crowd;
Now this was Jim's especial Foible,
He ran away when he was able,
And on this inauspicious day
He slipped his hand and ran away!
He hadn't gone a yard when—Bang!

With open Jaws, a Lion sprang,
And hungrily began to eat
The Boy: beginning at his feet.

Now, just imagine how it feels
When first your toes and then your heels,
And then by gradual degrees,
Your shins and ankles, calves and knees,
Are slowly eaten, bit by bit.
No wonder Jim detested it!
No wonder that he shouted "Hi!"
The Honest Keeper heard his cry,
Though very fat he almost ran
To help the little gentleman.
"Ponto!" he ordered as he came
(For Ponto was the Lion's name),
"Ponto!" he cried, with angry Frown,
"Let go, Sir! Down, Sir! Put it down!"

The Lion made a sudden stop,
He let the Dainty Morsel drop,
And slunk reluctant to his Cage,
Snarling with Disappointed Rage.
But when he bent him over Jim,
The Honest Keeper's Eyes were dim.
The Lion having reached his Head,
The Miserable Boy was dead!

When Nurse informed his Parents, they
Were more Concerned than I can say:
His Mother, as She dried her eyes,
Said, "Well—it gives me no surprise,
He would not do as he was told!"
His Father, who was self-controlled,
Bade all the children round attend
To James's miserable end,
And always keep a-hold of Nurse
For fear of finding something worse.

A Visit From Saint Nicholas
Clement Clarke Moore

'Twas the night before Christmas, when all through the house
Not a creature was stirring, not even a mouse;
The stockings were hung by the chimney with care,
In hopes that St Nicholas soon would be there;
The children were nestled all snug in their beds,
While visions of sugar-plums danced in their heads;
And mamma in her 'kerchief, and I in my cap,
Had just settled down for a long winter's nap –
When out on the lawn there arose such a clatter,
I sprang from the bed to see what was the matter.
Away to the window I flew like a flash,
Tore open the shutters, and threw up the sash.
The moon, on the breast of the new-fallen snow,
Gave the lustre of midday to objects below;
When what to my wondering eyes should appear,
But a miniature sleigh and eight tiny reindeer,
With a little old driver, so lively and quick,
I knew in a moment it must be Saint Nick.
More rapid than eagles his coursers they came,
And he whistled, and shouted, and called them by name:
"Now, *Dasher!* now, *Dancer!* now, *Prancer* and *Vixen!*

On, *Comet!* on *Cupid!* on, *Donder* and *Blitzen!*
To the top of the porch! to the top of the wall!
Now dash away! dash away! dash away all!"
As dry leaves that before the wild hurricane fly,
When they meet with an obstacle, mount to the sky;
So up to the house-top the coursers they flew
With the sleigh full of toys, and Saint Nicholas too.
And then, in a twinkling, I heard on the roof
The prancing and pawing of each little hoof –
As I drew in my head, and was turning around,
Down the chimney Saint Nicholas came with a bound.
He was dressed all in fur, from his head to his foot,
And his clothes were all tarnished with ashes and soot;
A bundle of toys he had flung on his back,
And he looked like a pedler just opening his pack.
His eyes – how they twinkled; his dimples, how merry!
His cheeks were like roses, his nose like a cherry!
His droll little mouth was drawn up like a bow,
And the beard of his chin was as white as the snow;
The stump of a pipe he held tight in his teeth,
And the smoke it encircled his head like a wreath;
He had a broad face and a little round belly,
That shook when he laughed, like a bowl full of jelly.
He was chubby and plump, a right jolly old elf,
And I laughed when I saw him, in spite of myself;
A wink of his eye and a twist of his head
Soon gave me to know I had nothing to dread;
He spoke not a word, but went straight to his work,

And filled all the stockings; then turned with a jerk,
And laying his finger aside of his nose,
And giving a nod, up the chimney he rose;
He sprang to his sleigh, to his team gave a whistle,
And away they all flew like the down of a thistle.
But I heard him exclaim, ere he drove out of sight,
"Happy Christmas to all, and to all a good-night!"

Hang up your stocking and be the Christmas star by learning this poem, and with it the names of all the reindeer.

Night Mail
W.H. Auden

I

This is the Night Mail crossing the Border,
Bringing the cheque and the postal order,
Letters for the rich, letters for the poor,
The shop at the corner, the girl next door.
Pulling up Beattock, a steady climb:
The gradient's against her, but she's on time.
Past cotton-grass and moorland boulder,
Shovelling white steam over her shoulder,
Snorting noisily as she passes
Silent miles of wind-bent grasses.
Birds turn their heads as she approaches,
Stare from the bushes at her blank-faced coaches.
Sheep-dogs cannot turn her course;
They slumber on with paws across.
In the farm she passes no one wakes,
But a jug in a bedroom gently shakes.

II

Dawn freshens. Her climb is done.

Down towards Glasgow she descends,

Towards the steam tugs yelping down a glade of cranes,

Towards the fields of apparatus, the furnaces

Set on the dark plain like gigantic chessmen.

All Scotland waits for her:

In dark glens, beside pale-green lochs,

Men long for news.

III

Letters of thanks, letters from banks,

Letters of joy from girl and boy,

Receipted bills and invitations

To inspect new stock or to visit relations,

And applications for situations,

And timid lovers' declarations,

And gossip, gossip from all the nations,

News circumstantial, news financial,

Letters with holiday snaps to enlarge in,

Letters with faces scrawled on the margin,

Letters from uncles, cousins and aunts,

Letters to Scotland from the South of France,

Letters of condolence to Highlands and Lowlands

Written on paper of every hue,

The pink, the violet, the white and the blue,

The chatty, the catty, the boring, the adoring,

The cold and official and the heart's outpouring,

Clever, stupid, short and long,
The typed and the printed and the spelt all wrong.

IV
Thousands are still asleep
Dreaming of terrifying monsters,
Or of friendly tea beside the band in Cranston's or Crawford's:
Asleep in working Glasgow, asleep in well-set Edinburgh,
Asleep in granite Aberdeen,
They continue their dreams,
But shall wake soon and long for letters,
And none will hear the postman's knock
Without a quickening of the heart.
For who can bear to feel himself forgotten?

The rhythm in this poem is so clever, it feels like being on a train. Read it out loud and you'll see for yourself.

Skimbleshanks: The Railway Cat
T.S. Eliot

There's a whisper down the line at 11.39
When the Night Mail's ready to depart,
Saying "Skimble where is Skimble has he gone to hunt the thimble?
We must find him or the train can't start."
All the guards and all the porters and the stationmaster's daughters
They are searching high and low,
Saying "Skimble where is Skimble for unless he's very nimble
Then the Night Mail just can't go."
At 11.42 then the signal's nearly due
And the passengers are frantic to a man –
Then Skimble will appear and he'll saunter to the rear:
He's been busy in the luggage van!
He gives one flash of his glass-green eyes
And the signal goes "All Clear!"
And we're off at last for the northern part
Of the Northern Hemisphere!

You may say that by and large it is Skimble who's in charge
Of the Sleeping Car Express.
From the driver and the guards to the bagmen playing cards
He will supervise them all, more or less.

Down the corridor he paces and examines all the faces
Of the travellers in the First and in the Third;
He establishes control by a regular patrol
And he'd know at once if anything occurred.
He will watch you without winking and he sees what you
    are thinking
And it's certain that he doesn't approve
Of hilarity and riot, so the folk are very quiet
When Skimble is about and on the move.
You can play no pranks with Skimbleshanks!
He's a Cat that cannot be ignored;
So nothing goes wrong on the Northern Mail
When Skimbleshanks is aboard.

Oh it's very pleasant when you have found your little den
With your name written up on the door.
And the berth is very neat with a newly folded sheet
And there's not a speck of dust on the floor.
There is every sort of light – you can make it dark or bright;
There's a button that you turn to make a breeze.
There's a funny little basin you're supposed to wash your face in
And a crank to shut the window if you sneeze.
Then the guard looks in politely and will ask you very brightly
"Do you like your morning tea weak or strong?"
But Skimble's just behind him and was ready to remind him,
For Skimble won't let anything go wrong.
And when you creep into your cosy berth
And pull up the counterpane,

You are bound to admit that it's very nice
To know that you won't be bothered by mice –
You can leave all that to the Railway Cat,
The Cat of the Railway Train!

In the middle of the night he is always fresh and bright;
Every now and then he has a cup of tea
With perhaps a drop of Scotch while he's keeping on the watch,
Only stopping here and there to catch a flea.
You were fast asleep at Crewe and so you never knew
That he was walking up and down the station;
You were sleeping all the while he was busy at Carlisle,
Where he greets the stationmaster with elation.
But you saw him at Dumfries, where he summons the police
If there's anything they ought to know about:
When you get to Gallowgate there you do not have to wait –
For Skimbleshanks will help you to get out!
He gives you a wave of his long brown tail
Which says: "I'll see you again!
You'll meet without fail on the Midnight Mail
The Cat of the Railway Train."

The Jumblies
Edward Lear

They went to sea in a Sieve, they did,
In a Sieve they went to sea:
In spite of all their friends could say,
On a winter's morn, on a stormy day,
In a Sieve they went to sea!
And when the Sieve turned round and round,
And every one cried, "You'll all be drowned!"
They called aloud, "Our Sieve ain't big,
But we don't care a button! We don't care a fig!
In a Sieve we'll go to sea!"
Far and few, far and few,
Are the lands where the Jumblies live;
Their heads are green, and their hands are blue,
And they went to sea in a Sieve.

They sailed away in a Sieve, they did,
In a Sieve they sailed so fast,
With only a beautiful pea-green veil
Tied with a riband by way of a sail,
To a small tobacco-pipe mast;
And every one said, who saw them go,

"O won't they be soon upset, you know!
For the sky is dark, and the voyage is long,
And happen what may, it's extremely wrong
In a Sieve to sail so fast!"
Far and few, far and few,
Are the lands where the Jumblies live;
Their heads are green, and their hands are blue,
And they went to sea in a Sieve.

The water it soon came in, it did,
The water it soon came in;
So to keep them dry, they wrapped their feet
In a pinky paper all folded neat,
And they fastened it down with a pin.
And they passed the night in a crockery-jar,
And each of them said, "How wise we are!
Though the sky be dark, and the voyage be long,
Yet we never can think we were rash or wrong,
While round in our Sieve we spin!"
Far and few, far and few,
Are the lands where the Jumblies live;
Their heads are green, and their hands are blue,
And they went to sea in a Sieve.

And all night long they sailed away;
And when the sun went down,
They whistled and warbled a moony song
To the echoing sound of a coppery gong,

In the shade of the mountains brown.
"O Timballo! How happy we are,
When we live in a Sieve and a crockery-jar,
And all night long in the moonlight pale,
We sail away with a pea-green sail,
In the shade of the mountains brown!"
Far and few, far and few,
Are the lands where the Jumblies live;
Their heads are green, and their hands are blue,
And they went to sea in a Sieve.

They sailed to the Western Sea, they did,
To a land all covered with trees,
And they bought an Owl, and a useful Cart,
And a pound of Rice, and a Cranberry Tart,
And a hive of silvery Bees.
And they bought a Pig, and some green Jack-daws,
And a lovely Monkey with lollipop paws,
And forty bottles of Ring-Bo-Ree,
And no end of Stilton Cheese.
Far and few, far and few,
Are the lands where the Jumblies live;
Their heads are green, and their hands are blue,
And they went to sea in a Sieve.

And in twenty years they all came back,
In twenty years or more,
And every one said, "How tall they've grown!

For they've been to the Lakes, and the Torrible Zone,
And the hills of the Chankly Bore!"
And they drank their health, and gave them a feast
Of dumplings made of beautiful yeast;
And every one said, "If we only live,
We too will go to sea in a Sieve,—
To the hills of the Chankly Bore!"
Far and few, far and few,
Are the lands where the Jumblies live;
Their heads are green, and their hands are blue,
And they went to sea in a Sieve.

*This was chosen by the late poet Adrian Mitchell "because
it is my favourite poem. It is about ridiculous creatures, like
me, who embark on seemingly impossible adventures and
win through happily".*

The Walrus and the Carpenter
Lewis Carroll

The sun was shining on the sea,
Shining with all his might:
He did his very best to make
The billows smooth and bright—
And this was odd, because it was
The middle of the night.

The moon was shining sulkily,
Because she thought the sun
Had got no business to be there
After the day was done—
"It's very rude of him," she said,
"To come and spoil the fun!"

The sea was wet as wet could be,
The sands were dry as dry.
You could not see a cloud, because
No cloud was in the sky:
No birds were flying overhead—
There were no birds to fly.

The Walrus and the Carpenter
Were walking close at hand;
They wept like anything to see
Such quantities of sand:
"If this were only cleared away,"
They said, "it would be grand!"

"If seven maids with seven mops
Swept it for half a year.
Do you suppose," the Walrus said,
"That they could get it clear?"
"I doubt it," said the Carpenter,
And shed a bitter tear.

"O Oysters, come and walk with us!"
The Walrus did beseech.
"A pleasant walk, a pleasant talk,
Along the briny beach:
We cannot do with more than four,
To give a hand to each."

The eldest Oyster looked at him,
But never a word he said:
The eldest Oyster winked his eye,
And shook his heavy head—
Meaning to say he did not choose
To leave the oyster-bed.

But four young Oysters hurried up,
All eager for the treat:
Their coats were brushed, their faces washed,
Their shoes were clean and neat—
And this was odd, because, you know,
They hadn't any feet.

Four other Oysters followed them,
And yet another four;
And thick and fast they came at last,
And more, and more, and more—
All hopping through the frothy waves,
And scrambling to the shore.

The Walrus and the Carpenter
Walked on a mile or so,
And then they rested on a rock
Conveniently low:
And all the little Oysters stood
And waited in a row.

"The time has come," the Walrus said,
"To talk of many things:
Of shoes—and ships—and sealing-wax—
Of cabbages—and kings—
And why the sea is boiling hot—
And whether pigs have wings."

"But wait a bit," the Oysters cried,
"Before we have our chat;
For some of us are out of breath,
And all of us are fat!"
"No hurry!" said the Carpenter.
They thanked him much for that.

"A loaf of bread," the Walrus said,
"Is what we chiefly need:
Pepper and vinegar besides
Are very good indeed—
Now if you're ready, Oysters dear,
We can begin to feed."

"But not on us!" the Oysters cried,
Turning a little blue.
"After such kindness, that would be
A dismal thing to do!"
"The night is fine," the Walrus said.
Do you admire the view?

"It was so kind of you to come!
And you are very nice!"
The Carpenter said nothing but
"Cut us another slice:
I wish you were not quite so deaf—
I've had to ask you twice!"

"It seems a shame," the Walrus said,
"To play them such a trick,
After we've brought them out so far,
And made them trot so quick!"
The Carpenter said nothing but
"The butter's spread too thick!"

"I weep for you," the Walrus said:
"I deeply sympathize."
With sobs and tears he sorted out
Those of the largest size,
Holding his pocket-handkerchief
Before his streaming eyes.

"O Oysters," said the Carpenter,
"You've had a pleasant run!
Shall we be trotting home again?'
But answer came there none—
And this was scarcely odd, because
They'd eaten every one.

The writer Frank Cottrell Boyce chose this. He likes it "because it's less well known than Jabberwocky, but it's just as funny and because there are two characters in it so you get to do two voices and also pretend to weep".

Section 3

Jump

Jump into the deep end with something more challenging!

Our Revels Now Are Ended
William Shakespeare

Our revels now are ended. These our actors,
As I foretold you, were all spirits, and
Are melted into air, into thin air:
And, like the baseless fabric of this vision,
The cloud-capp'd towers, the gorgeous palaces,
The solemn temples, the great globe itself,
Yea, all which it inherit, shall dissolve,
And, like this insubstantial pageant faded,
Leave not a rack behind. We are such stuff
As dreams are made on; and our little life
Is rounded with a sleep.

A version of these lines of Prospero from the play The Tempest *appear on the memorial to Shakespeare in Westminster Abbey. The "great globe" may be a reference to the Globe Theatre in Southwark, where many of Shakespeare's plays were performed.*

Free
Eugene O'Neill

Weary am I of the tumult, sick of the staring crowd,
Pining for wild sea places where the soul may think aloud.
Fled is the glamour of cities, dead as the ghost of a dream,
While I pine anew for the tint of blue on the breast of the
old Gulf Stream.

I have had my dance with Folly, nor do I shirk the blame;
I have sipped the so-called Wine of Life and paid the price of shame;
But I know that I shall find surcease, the rest my spirit craves,
Where the rainbows play in the flying spray,
'Mid the keen salt kiss of the waves.

Then it's ho! for the plunging deck of a bark, the hoarse
song of the crew,
With never a thought of those we left or what we are going to do;
Nor heed the old ship's burning, but break the shackles of care
And at last be free, on the open sea, with the trade wind in our hair.

Ozymandias
Percy Bysshe Shelley

I met a traveller from an antique land
Who said: Two vast and trunkless legs of stone
Stand in the desert. . . Near them, on the sand,
Half sunk, a shatter'd visage lies, whose frown
And wrinkled lip and sneer of cold command,
Tell that its sculptor well those passions read
Which yet survive, stamp'd on these lifeless things,
The hand that mock'd them, and the heart that fed:
And on the pedestal these words appear:
"My name is Ozymandias, king of kings:
Look on my works, ye mighty, and despair!"
Nothing beside remains. Round the decay
Of that colossal wreck, boundless and bare,
The lone and level sands stretch far away.

The writer Louis de Bernières chose this poem "as it's a good incentive to modesty".

Sonnet 29
William Shakespeare

When, in disgrace with Fortune and men's eyes
I all alone beweep my outcast state,
And trouble deaf heav'n with my bootless cries,
And look upon myself, and curse my fate,
Wishing me like to one more rich in hope,
Featured like him, like him with friends possessed,
Desiring this man's art and that man's scope,
With what I most enjoy contented least;
Yet in these thoughts myself almost despising,
Haply I think on thee, and then my state,
Like to the lark at break of day arising,
From sullen earth, sings hymns at heaven's gate;
For thy sweet love remembered such wealth brings,
That then I scorn to change my state with kings.

*Shakespeare wrote lots of plays, but did you know that he is
also famous for writing sonnets? Here is a very well-known
one.*

Anthem for Doomed Youth
Wilfred Owen

What passing-bells for these who die as cattle?
Only the monstrous anger of the guns.
Only the stuttering rifles' rapid rattle
Can patter out their hasty orisons.
No mockeries now for them; no prayers nor bells,
Nor any voice of mourning save the choirs, –
The shrill, demented choirs of wailing shells;
And bugles calling for them from sad shires.

What candles may be held to speed them all?
Not in the hands of boys, but in their eyes
Shall shine the holy glimmers of good-byes.
The pallor of girls' brows shall be their pall;
Their flowers the tenderness of patient minds,
And each slow dusk a drawing-down of blinds.

*The writer Anthony Horowitz chose this poem because it
"was written about the First World War, but it could apply
to any war. It is short and very rhythmic, making it easy
to learn. I think it's a wonderful poem and the last line in
particular has an extraordinary resonance".*

High Flight (An Airman's Ecstasy)
John Gillespie Magee

Oh, I have slipped the surly bonds of earth
And danced the skies on laughter-silvered wings;
Sunward I've climbed and joined the tumbling mirth
Of sun-split clouds—and done a hundred things
You have not dreamed of; wheeled and soared and swung
High in the sunlit silence. Hovering there
I've chased the shouting wind along, and flung
My eager craft through footless halls of air;
Up, up the long, delirious, burning blue
I've topped the wind-swept heights with easy grace,
Where never lark nor even eagle flew;
And while, with silent lifting mind I've trod
The high untrespassed sanctity of space,
Put out my hand, and touched the face of God.

American President Ronald Reagan quoted from this poem in his
speech following the 1986 Challenger Space Shuttle disaster.

Sonnet 18
William Shakespeare

Shall I compare thee to a summer's day?
Thou art more lovely and more temperate:
Rough winds do shake the darling buds of May,
And summer's lease hath all too short a date:
Sometime too hot the eye of heaven shines,
And often is his gold complexion dimmed;
And every fair from fair sometime declines,
By chance, or nature's changing course, untrimmed:
But thy eternal summer shall not fade,
Nor lose possession of that fair thou ow'st,
Nor shall Death brag thou wander'st in his shade
When in eternal lines to time thou grow'st:
So long as men can breathe or eyes can see,
So long lives this, and this gives life to thee.

Sonnet 43
Elizabeth Barrett Browning

How do I love thee? Let me count the ways.
I love thee to the depth and breadth and height
My soul can reach, when feeling out of sight
For the ends of Being and ideal Grace.
I love thee to the level of every day's
Most quiet need, by sun and candlelight.
I love thee freely, as men strive for Right;
I love thee purely, as they turn from Praise.
I love thee with the passion put to use
In my old griefs, and with my childhood's faith.
I love thee with a love I seemed to lose
With my lost saints,—I love thee with the breath,
Smiles, tears, of all my life!—and, if God choose,
I shall but love thee better after death.

This touching sonnet was written by the Victorian poet Elizabeth Barrett Browning at the age of 40, after she fell in love with Robert Browning. The poem is full of her astonishment and wonder at finding such passion in adulthood. Robert Browning persuaded Elizabeth to publish this and the other Sonnets From the Portuguese *after their marriage. The poems became instantly successful.*

Spring and Fall
(to a young child)
Gerard Manley Hopkins

Margaret, are you grieving
Over Goldengrove unleaving?
Leaves, like the things of man, you
With your fresh thoughts care for, can you?
Ah! as the heart grows older
It will come to such sights colder
By and by, nor spare a sigh
Though worlds of wanwood leafmeal lie;
And yet you will weep and know why.
Now no matter, child, the name:
Sorrow's springs are the same.
Nor mouth had, no nor mind, expressed
What heart heard of, ghost guessed:
It is the blight man was born for,
It is Margaret you mourn for.

Margaret cries over the falling leaves. Hopkins makes the rather gloomy point that this is the first of many things she will cry for, that learning about mortality is an inevitable part of growing up.

Inversnaid

Gerard Manley Hopkins

This darksome burn, horseback brown,
His rollrock highroad roaring down,
In coop and in comb the fleece of his foam
Flutes and low to the lake falls home.

A windpuff-bonnet of fawn-froth
Turns and twindles over the broth
Of a pool so pitchblack, fell-frowning,
It rounds and rounds Despair to drowning.

Degged with dew, dappled with dew
Are the groins of the braes that the brook treads through,
Wiry heathpacks, flitches of fern,
And the beadbonny ash that sits over the burn.

What would the world be, once bereft
Of wet and of wildness? Let them be left,
O let them be left, wildness and wet;
Long live the weeds and the wilderness yet.

You can hear the crashing sounds of the waterfall in this beautiful poem.

The Death of Hector
Homer, adapted from the translation by Richard Lattimore

So he spoke, and balanced the spear far shadowed, and threw it,
and struck in the middle of Achilles' shield, nor missed it,
but the spear was driven far back from the shield, and
    Hector was angered
because his swift weapon had been loosed from his hand in
    a vain cast.
He stood discouraged, and had no other ash spear;
but lifting his voice he called aloud on Deiphobus of the pale
    shield,
and asked him for a long spear but Deiphobus was not near him.
And Hector knew the truth inside his heart and spoke aloud:
"No use. Here at last the gods have called me deathward.
I thought the hero Deiphobus was here close beside me
but he is he behind the wall and it was Athena cheating me,
and now evil death is close to me, and no longer far away,
and there is no way out. So it must long since have been pleasing
to Zeus and Zeus' son who strikes from afar, this way;
    though before this
they defended me gladly. But now my fate is upon me.
Let me at least not die without a struggle, inglorious,
but do a big thing first, that men to come shall know of it."

The Mayor of London, Boris Johnson, chose the ancient Greek poem The Iliad as his favourite. This extract is from the twelfth book. He says it "teaches you all you need to know about life and death and the importance of failure".

Love
George Herbert

Love bade me welcome; yet my soul drew back,
    Guilty of dust and sin.
But quick-eye Love, observing me grow slack
    From my first entrance in,
Drew nearer to me, sweetly questioning
    If I lack'd anything.

"A guest," I answer'd, "worthy to be here:"
    Love said, "you shall be he."
"I, the unkind, ungrateful? Ah, my dear,
    I cannot look on thee."
Love took my hand and smiling did reply,
    "Who made the eyes but I?"

"Truth, Lord, but I have marr'd them: let my shame
    Go where it doth deserve."
"And know you not," says Love, "Who bore the blame?"
    "My dear, then I will serve."
"You must sit down," says Love, "and taste my meat."
    So I did sit and eat.

War Song Of The Saracens
James Elroy Flecker

We are they who come faster than fate: we are they who
    ride early or late:
We storm at your ivory gate: Pale Kings of the Sunset, beware!
Not on silk nor in samet we lie, not in curtained solemnity die
Among women who chatter and cry, and children who
    mumble a prayer.
But we sleep by the ropes of the camp, and we rise with a
    shout, and we tramp
With the sun or the moon for a lamp, and the spray of the
    wind in our hair.

From the lands, where the elephants are, to the forts of
    Merou and Balghar,
Our steel we have brought and our star to shine on the ruins
    of Rum.
We have marched from the Indus to Spain, and by God we
    will go there again;
We have stood on the shore of the plain where the Waters
    of Destiny boom.

A mart of destruction we made at Jalula where men were
   afraid,
For death was a difficult trade, and the sword was a broker
   of doom;

And the Spear was a Desert Physician who cured not a few
   of ambition,
And drave not a few to perdition with medicine bitter and strong:
And the shield was a grief to the fool and as bright as a
   desolate pool,
And as straight as the rock of Stamboul when their cavalry
   thundered along:
For the coward was drowned with the brave when our
   battle sheered up like a wave,
And the dead to the desert we gave, and the glory to God
   in our song.

*The writer Joanna Trollope says that she "chose this poem
because it is gorgeously unashamedly romantic, and it
is impossible not to march about if you are reciting it out
loud".*

"On Wenlock Edge"
A. E. Housman

On Wenlock Edge the wood's in trouble;
His forest fleece the Wrekin heaves;
The gale, it plies the saplings double,
And thick on Severn snow the leaves.
'Twould blow like this through holt and hanger
When Uricon the city stood:
'Tis the old wind in the old anger,
But then it threshed another wood.
Then, 'twas before my time, the Roman
At yonder heaving hill would stare:
The blood that warms an English yeoman,
The thoughts that hurt him, they were there.
There, like the wind through woods in riot,
Through him the gale of life blew high;
The tree of man was never quiet:
Then 'twas the Roman, now 'tis I.
The gale, it plies the saplings double,
It blows so hard, 'twill soon be gone:
To-day the Roman and his trouble
Are ashes under Uricon.

Uricon was a Roman fortress built to withstand the Welsh hill tribes. Housman observes that the storm he sees lashing the woods on Wenlock Edge would have been experienced with exactly the same fear and wonder by Roman Legionaries fifteen-hundred years ago.

The Tyger
William Blake

Tyger! Tyger! burning bright
In the forests of the night,
What immortal hand or eye
Could frame thy fearful symmetry?

In what distant deeps or skies
Burnt the fire of thine eyes?
On what wings dare he aspire?
What the hand dare seize the fire?

And what shoulder, and what art,
Could twist the sinews of thy heart?
And when thy heart began to beat,
What dread hand? and what dread feet?

What the hammer? what the chain?
In what furnace was thy brain?
What the anvil? what dread grasp?
Dare its deadly terrors clasp?

When the stars threw down their spears,
And water'd heaven with their tears,
Did he smile his work to see?
Did he who made the Lamb make thee?

Tyger! Tyger! burning bright
In the forests of the night,
What immortal hand or eye
Dare frame thy fearful symmetry?

First Love
John Clare

I ne'er was struck before that hour
With love so sudden and so sweet,
Her face it bloomed like a sweet flower
And stole my heart away complete.
My face turned pale as deadly pale,
My legs refused to walk away,
And when she looked, what could I ail?
My life and all seemed turned to clay.

And then my blood rushed to my face
And took my eyesight quite away,
The trees and bushes round the place
Seemed midnight at noonday.
I could not see a single thing,
Words from my eyes did start—
They spoke as chords do from the string,
And blood burnt round my heart.

Are flowers the winter's choice?
Is love's bed always snow?
She seemed to hear my silent voice,
Not love's appeals to know.
I never saw so sweet a face
As that I stood before.
My heart has left its dwelling-place
And can return no more.

This poem perfectly sums up the heart-stopping, tummy-tickling feelings of falling in love.

The Flea
John Donne

Mark but this flea, and mark in this,
How little that which thou deniest me is;
Me it suck'd first, and now sucks thee,
And in this flea, our two bloods mingled be;
Confess it, this cannot be said
A sin, or shame, or loss of maidenhead,
Yet this enjoys before it woo,
And pamper'd swells with one blood made of two,
And this, alas, is more than we would do.

O stay, three lives in one flea spare,
Where we almost, nay more than married are:
This flea is you and I, and this
Our marriage bed, and marriage temple is;
Though parents grudge, and you, we're met,
And cloister'd in these living walls of jet.
Though use make thee apt to kill me,
Let not to this, self-murder added be,
And sacrilege, three sins in killing three.

Cruel and sudden, has thou since
Purpled thy nail, in blood of innocence?
In what could this flea guilty be,
Except in that drop which it suck'd from thee?
Yet thou triumph'st, and say'st that thou
Find'st not thyself, nor me the weaker now;
'Tis true, then learn how false fears be;
Just so much honor, when thou yield'st to me,
Will waste, as this flea's death took life from thee.

This is a hard poem to remember, but it's worth reading aloud and enjoying the old-fashioned language.

The Seven Ages Of Man
William Shakespeare

All the world's a stage,
And all the men and women merely players.
They have their exits and their entrances,
And one man in his time plays many parts,
His acts being seven ages. At first the infant,
Mewling and puking in the nurse's arms.
Then, the whining school-boy with his satchel
And shining morning face, creeping like snail
Unwillingly to school. And then the lover,
Sighing like furnace, with a woeful ballad
Made to his mistress' eyebrow. Then, a soldier,
Full of strange oaths, and bearded like the pard,
Jealous in honour, sudden and quick in quarrel,
Seeking the bubble reputation
Even in the cannon's mouth. And then, the justice,
In fair round belly, with good capon lin'd,
With eyes severe, and beard of formal cut,
Full of wise saws, and modern instances,
And so he plays his part. The sixth age shifts
Into the lean and slipper'd pantaloon,
With spectacles on nose, and pouch on side,

His youthful hose well sav'd, a world too wide
For his shrunk shank, and his big manly voice,
Turning again toward childish treble, pipes
And whistles in his sound. Last scene of all,
That ends this strange eventful history,
Is second childishness and mere oblivion,
Sans teeth, sans eyes, sans taste, sans everything.

This extract is from Shakespeare's play **As You Like It.** *The opening lines are very famous. Recite the first to your teacher and see how much of the poem he or she knows.*

Dulce Et Decorum Est
Wilfred Owen

Bent double, like old beggars under sacks,
Knock-kneed, coughing like hags, we cursed through sludge,
Till on the haunting flares we turned our backs
And towards our distant rest began to trudge.
Men marched asleep. Many had lost their boots,
But limped on, blood-shod. All went lame; all blind;
Drunk with fatigue; deaf even to the hoots
Of gas-shells dropping softly behind.

Gas! Gas! Quick, boys! – An ecstasy of fumbling,
Fitting the clumsy helmets just in time
But someone still was yelling out and stumbling
And flound'ring like a man in fire or lime. –
Dim, through the misty panes and thick green light
As under a green sea, I saw him drowning.

In all my dreams before my helpless sight
He plunges at me, guttering, choking, drowning.

If in some smothering dreams, you too could pace
Behind the wagon that we flung him in,

And watch the white eyes writhing in his face,
His hanging face, like a devil's sick of sin;
If you could hear, at every jolt, the blood
Come gargling from the froth-corrupted lungs,
Obscene as cancer, bitter as the cud
Of vile, incurable sores on innocent tongues,–
My friend, you would not tell with such high zest
To children ardent for some desperate glory,
The old lie: *Dulce et decorum est*
Pro patria mori.

The Right Honourable David Cameron MP chose this poem.
"I remember when I first read it – and had to learn it – I found
it an incredibly powerful poem about war. The imagery it
summons up is quite shocking and has stayed with me ever
since."

Lepanto
G.K. Chesterton

White founts falling in the courts of the sun,
And the Soldan of Byzantium is smiling as they run;
There is laughter like the fountains in that face of all men feared,
It stirs the forest darkness, the darkness of his beard,
It curls the blood-red crescent, the crescent of his lips,
For the inmost sea of all the earth is shaken with his ships.
They have dared the white republics up the capes of Italy,
They have dashed the Adriatic round the Lion of the Sea,
And the Pope has cast his arms abroad for agony and loss,
And called the kings of Christendom for swords about the Cross,
The cold queen of England is looking in the glass;
The shadow of the Valois is yawning at the Mass;
From evening isles fantastical rings faint the Spanish gun,
And the Lord upon the Golden Horn is laughing in the sun.

Dim drums throbbing, in the hills half heard,
Where only on a nameless throne a crownless prince has stirred,
Where, risen from a doubtful seat and half-attainted stall,
The last knight of Europe takes weapons from the wall,
The last and lingering troubadour to whom the bird has sung,
That once went singing southward when all the world was young.

In that enormous silence, tiny and unafraid,
Comes up along a winding road the noise of the Crusade.
Strong gongs groaning as the guns boom far,
Don John of Austria is going to the war,
Stiff flags straining in the night-blasts cold
In the gloom black-purple, in the glint old-gold,
Torchlight crimson on the copper kettle-drums,
Then the tuckets, then the trumpets, then the cannon, and
    he comes.
Don John laughing in the brave beard curled,
Spurning of his stirrups like the thrones of all the world,
Holding his head up for a flag of all the free.
Love-light of Spain – hurrah!
Death-light of Africa!
Don John of Austria
Is riding to the sea.

Another poem that's quite challenging to learn. But have a go!

The Listeners
Walter De La Mare

"Is there anybody there?" said the Traveller,
  Knocking on the moonlit door;
And his horse in the silence champed the grasses
  Of the forest's ferny floor:
And a bird flew up out of the turret,
  Above the Traveller's head:
And he smote upon the door again a second time;
  "Is there anybody there?" he said.
But no one descended to the Traveller;
  No head from the leaf-fringed sill
Leaned over and looked into his grey eyes,
  Where he stood perplexed and still.
But only a host of phantom listeners
  That dwelt in the lone house then
Stood listening in the quiet of the moonlight
  To that voice from the world of men:
Stood thronging the faint moonbeams on the dark stair,
  That goes down to the empty hall,
Hearkening in an air stirred and shaken
  By the lonely Traveller's call.
And he felt in his heart their strangeness,

Their stillness answering his cry,
While his horse moved, cropping the dark turf,
   'Neath the starred and leafy sky;
For he suddenly smote on the door, even
   Louder, and lifted his head: –
"Tell them I came, and no one answered,
   That I kept my word," he said.
Never the least stir made the listeners,
   Though every word he spake
Fell echoing through the shadowiness of the still house
   From the one man left awake:
Ay, they heard his foot upon the stirrup,
   And the sound of iron on stone,
And how the silence surged softly backward,
   When the plunging hoofs were gone.

This haunting poem is full of atmosphere and tension. Learn it, and recite it in the dark!

The Nightmare
W.S. Gilbert

When you're lying awake with a dismal headache, and
    repose is taboo'd by anxiety,
I conceive you may use any language you choose to indulge
    in, without impropriety;
For your brain is on fire – the bedclothes conspire of your
    usual slumber to plunder you:
First your counterpane goes, and uncovers your toes, and
    your sheet slips demurely from under you;
Then the blanketing tickles – you feel like mixed pickles – so
    terribly sharp is the pricking,
And you're hot, and you're cross, and you tumble and toss
    till there's nothing 'twixt you and the ticking.
Then the bedclothes all creep to the ground in a heap, and
    you pick 'em all up in a tangle;
Next your pillow resigns and politely declines to remain at
    its usual angle!
Well, you get some repose in the form of a doze, with hot
    eyeballs and head ever aching,
But your slumbering teems with such horrible dreams that
    you'd very much better be waking;
For you dream you are crossing the Channel, and tossing
    about in a steamer from Harwich –

Which is something between a large bathing machine and a
  very small second-class carriage –
And you're giving a treat (penny ice and cold meat) to a
  party of friends and relations –
They're a ravenous horde – and they all came on board at
  Sloane Square and South Kensington Stations.
And bound on that journey you find your attorney (who
  started that morning from Devon);
He's a bit undersized, and you don't feel surprised when he
  tells you he's only eleven.
Well, you're driving like mad with this singular lad (by-the-
  bye the ship's now a four-wheeler),
And you're playing round games, and he calls you bad
  names when you tell him that "ties pay the dealer";
But this you can't stand, so you throw up your hand, and
  you find you're as cold as an icicle,
In your shirt and your socks (the black silk with gold clocks),
  crossing Salisbury Plain on a bicycle:
And he and the crew are on bicycles too – which they've
  somehow or other invested in –
And he's telling the tars, all the particulars of a company
  he's interested in –
It's a scheme of devices, to get at low prices, all goods from
  cough mixtures to cables
(Which tickled the sailors), by treating retailers as though
  they were all vegetables:
You get a good spadesman to plant a small tradesman (first
  take off his boots with a boot-tree)

And his legs will take root, and his fingers will shoot, and
　　they'll blossom and bud like a fruit-tree –
From the greengrocer tree you get grapes and green pea,
　　cauliflower, pineapple, and cranberries,
While the pastrycook plant, cherry brandy will grant, apple
　　puffs, and three-corners, and banberries –
The shares are a penny, and ever so many are taken by
　　Rothschild and Baring,
And just as a few are allotted to you, you awake with a
　　shudder despairing –
You're a regular wreck, with a crick in your neck, and no
　　wonder you snore, for your head's on the floor, and
　　you've needles and pins from your soles to your shins,
　　and your flesh is a-creep, for your left leg's asleep, and
　　you've cramp in your toes, and a fly on your nose, and
　　some fluff in your lung, and a feverish tongue, and a
　　thirst that's intense, and a general sense that you haven't
　　been sleeping in clover;
But the darkness has passed, and it's daylight at last, and the
　　night has been long –
Ditto my song – and thank goodness they're both of them over!

*W.S. Gilbert was one half of the successful musical part-
nership Gilbert and Sullivan.* **The Nightmare** *comes from
their comic opera* Iolanthe. *Learn it when you can't sleep at
night.*

"Thrice the brinded cat hath mew'd"
William Shakespeare

Thrice the brinded cat hath mew'd.
Thrice and once the hedge-pig whined.
Harpier cries 'Tis time, 'tis time.
Round about the cauldron go;
In the poison'd entrails throw.
Toad, that under cold stone
Days and nights has thirty-one
Swelter'd venom sleeping got,
Boil thou first i' the charmed pot.
    Double, double toil and trouble;
    Fire burn, and cauldron bubble.

Fillet of a fenny snake,
In the cauldron boil and bake;
Eye of newt and toe of frog,
Wool of bat and tongue of dog,
Adder's fork and blind-worm's sting,
Lizard's leg and owlet's wing,
For a charm of powerful trouble,
Like a hell-broth boil and bubble.
    Double, double toil and trouble;
    Fire burn and cauldron bubble.

Scale of dragon, tooth of wolf,
Witches' mummy, maw and gulf
Of the ravin'd salt-sea shark,
Root of hemlock digg'd i' the dark,
Liver of blaspheming Jew,
Gall of goat, and slips of yew
Silver'd in the moon's eclipse,
Nose of Turk and Tartar's lips,
Finger of birth-strangled babe
Ditch-deliver'd by a drab,
Make the gruel thick and slab:
Add thereto a tiger's chaudron,
For the ingredients of our cauldron.
　　Double, double toil and trouble;
　　Fire burn and cauldron bubble.
　　Cool it with a baboon's blood,
　　Then the charm is firm and good.

The perfect Hallowe'en poem! These are the lines of the three witches in Shakespeare's play **Macbeth.**

Medusa
Carol Ann Duffy

A suspicion, a doubt, a jealousy
grew in my mind,
which turned the hairs on my head to filthy snakes
as though my thoughts
hissed and spat on my scalp.

My bride's breath soured, stank
in the grey bags of my lungs.
I'm foul mouthed now, foul tongued,
yellow fanged.
There are bullet tears in my eyes.
Are you terrified?

Be terrified.
It's you I love,
perfect man, Greek God, my own;
but I know you'll go, betray me, stray
from home.
So better by far for me if you were stone.

I glanced at a buzzing bee,
a dull grey pebble fell
to the ground.
I glanced at a singing bird,
a handful of dusty gravel
spattered down.

I looked at a ginger cat,
a housebrick
shattered a bowl of milk.
I looked at a snuffling pig,
a boulder rolled
in a heap of shit.

I stared in the mirror.
Love gone bad
showed me a Gorgon.
I stared at a dragon.
Fire spewed
from the mouth of a mountain.

And here you come
with a shield for a heart
and a sword for a tongue
and your girls, your girls.
Wasn't I beautiful
Wasn't I fragrant and young?

Look at me now.

A Musical Instrument
Elizabeth Barrett Browning

What was he doing, the great god Pan,
    Down in the reeds by the river?
Spreading ruin and scattering ban,
Splashing and paddling with hoofs of a goat,
And breaking the golden lilies afloat
    With the dragon-fly on the river.

He tore out a reed, the great god Pan,
    From the deep cool bed of the river:
The limpid water turbidly ran,
And the broken lilies a-dying lay,
And the dragon-fly had fled away,
    Ere he brought it out of the river.

High on the shore sat the great god Pan,
    While turbidly flowed the river;
And hacked and hewed as a great god can,
With his hard bleak steel at the patient reed,
Till there was not a sign of the leaf indeed
    To prove it fresh from the river.

He cut it short, did the great god Pan,
    (How tall it stood in the river!)
Then drew the pith, like the heart of a man,
Steadily from the outside ring,
And notched the poor dry empty thing
    In holes, as he sat by the river.

"This is the way," laughed the great god Pan.
    (Laughed while he sat by the river,)
"The only way, since gods began
To make sweet music, they could succeed."
Then, dropping his mouth to a hole in the reed,
    He blew in power by the river.

Sweet, sweet, sweet, O Pan!
    Piercing sweet by the river!
Blinding sweet, O great god Pan!
The sun on the hill forgot to die,
And the lilies revived, and the dragon-fly
    Came back to dream on the river.

Yet half a beast is the great god Pan,
    To laugh as he sits by the river,
Making a poet out of a man:
The true gods sigh for the cost and pain,—
For the reed which grows nevermore again
    As a reed with the reeds in the river.

Still I Rise

Maya Angelou

You may write me down in history
With your bitter, twisted lies,
You may trod me in the very dirt
But still, like dust, I'll rise.

Does my sassiness upset you?
Why are you beset with gloom?
'Cause I walk like I've got oil wells
Pumping in my living room.

Just like moons and like suns,
With the certainty of tides,
Just like hopes springing high,
Still I'll rise.

Did you want to see me broken?
Bowed head and lowered eyes?
Shoulders falling down like teardrops,
Weakened by my soulful cries?

Does my haughtiness offend you?
Don't you take it awful hard
'Cause I laugh like I've got gold mines
Diggin' in my own back yard.

You may shoot me with your words,
You may cut me with your eyes,
You may kill me with your hatefulness,
But still, like air, I'll rise.

Does my sexiness upset you?
Does it come as a surprise
That I dance like I've got diamonds
At the meeting of my thighs?

Out of the huts of history's shame
I rise
Up from a past that's rooted in pain
I rise
I'm a black ocean, leaping and wide,
Welling and swelling I bear in the tide.

Leaving behind nights of terror and fear
I rise
Into a daybreak that's wondrously clear
I rise
Bringing the gifts that my ancestors gave,
I am the dream and the hope of the slave.

I rise
I rise
I rise.

This poem is Maya Angelou's personal manifesto – an expression of her extraordinary zest for life. Famous since its publication, it has been adopted by women everywhere as a personal theme song.

A Subaltern's Love Song
Sir John Betjeman

Miss J. Hunter Dunn, Miss J. Hunter Dunn,
Furnish'd and burnish'd by Aldershot sun,
What strenuous singles we played after tea,
We in the tournament – you against me!

Love-thirty, love-forty, oh! weakness of joy,
The speed of a swallow, the grace of a boy,
With carefullest carelessness, gaily you won,
I am weak from your loveliness, Joan Hunter Dunn.

Miss Joan Hunter Dunn, Miss Joan Hunter Dunn,
How mad I am, sad I am, glad that you won.
The warm-handled racket is back in its press,
But my shock-headed victor, she loves me no less.

Her father's euonymus shines as we walk,
And swing past the summer-house, buried in talk,
And cool the verandah that welcomes us in
To the six-o'clock news and a lime-juice and gin.

The scent of the conifers, sound of the bath,
The view from my bedroom of moss-dappled path,
As I struggle with double-end evening tie,
For we dance at the Golf Club, my victor and I.

On the floor of her bedroom lie blazer and shorts
And the cream-coloured walls are be-trophied with sports,
And westering, questioning settles the sun
On your low-leaded window, Miss Joan Hunter Dunn.

The Hillman is waiting, the light's in the hall,
The pictures of Egypt are bright on the wall,
My sweet, I am standing beside the oak stair
And there on the landing's the light on your hair.

By roads "not adopted", by woodlanded ways,
She drove to the club in the late summer haze,
Into nine-o'clock Camberley, heavy with bells
And mushroomy, pine-woody, evergreen smells.

Miss Joan Hunter Dunn, Miss Joan Hunter Dunn,
I can hear from the car-park the dance has begun.
Oh! full Surrey twilight! importunate band!
Oh! strongly adorable tennis-girl's hand!

Around us are Rovers and Austins afar,
Above us, the intimate roof of the car,
And here on my right is the girl of my choice,
With the tilt of her nose and the chime of her voice.

And the scent of her wrap, and the words never said,
And the ominous, ominous dancing ahead.
We sat in the car-park till twenty to one
And now I'm engaged to Miss Joan Hunter Dunn.

This poem is bursting with the energy of falling in love.

The Raven
Edgar Allan Poe

Once upon a midnight dreary, while I pondered, weak and weary,
Over many a quaint and curious volume of forgotten lore,—
While I nodded, nearly napping, suddenly there came a tapping,
As of some one gently rapping, rapping at my chamber door.
"'Tis some visitor," I muttered, "tapping at my chamber door —
 Only this and nothing more."

Ah, distinctly I remember, it was in the bleak December,
And each separate dying ember wrought its ghost upon the floor.
Eagerly I wished the morrow;—vainly I had sought to borrow
From my books surcease of sorrow—sorrow for the lost Lenore—
For the rare and radiant maiden whom the angels name Lenore—
 Nameless here for evermore.

And the silken sad uncertain rustling of each purple curtain
Thrilled me—filled me with fantastic terrors never felt before;
So that now, to still the beating of my heart, I stood repeating
"'Tis some visitor entreating entrance at my chamber door—
Some late visitor entreating entrance at my chamber door;—
 This it is and nothing more."

Presently my soul grew stronger; hesitating then no longer,
"Sir," said I, "or, Madam, truly your forgiveness I implore;
But the fact is I was napping, and so gently you came rapping,
And so faintly you came tapping, – tapping at my chamber door,
That I scarce was sure I heard you"—here I opened wide
    the door:—
    Darkness there and nothing more.

Deep into that darkness peering, long I stood there
    wondering, fearing,
Doubting, dreaming dreams no mortal ever dared to dream
    before;
But the silence was unbroken, and the darkness gave no token,
And the only word there spoken was the whispered word,
    "Lenore!"
This I whispered, and an echo murmured back the word,
    "Lenore!"—
    Merely this and nothing more.

Then into the chamber turning, all my soul within me burning,
Soon I heard again a tapping somewhat louder than before.
"Surely," said I, "surely that is something at my window lattice;
Let me see, then, what thereat is, and this mystery explore—
Let my heart be still a moment, and this mystery explore;—
    'Tis the wind and nothing more!"

Open here I flung the shutter, when, with many a flirt and flutter,
In there stepped a stately Raven of the saintly days of yore.

Not the least obeisance made he; not an instant stopped or
    stayed he;
But, with mien of lord or lady, perched above my chamber
    door—
Perched upon a bust of Pallas just above my chamber door—
    Perched, and sat, and nothing more.

Then this ebony bird beguiling my sad fancy into smiling,
By the grave and stern decorum of the countenance it wore,
"Though thy crest be shorn and shaven, thou," I said, "art
    sure no craven,
Ghastly grim and ancient Raven wandering from the
    Nightly shore —
Tell me what thy Lordly name is on the Night's Plutonian shore!"
    Quoth the Raven, "Nevermore."

These lines are taken from **The Raven,** *one of the most
famous and chilling poems ever written.*

The Pied Piper Of Hamelin
Robert Browning

Into the street the Piper stept,
Smiling first a little smile,
As if he knew what magic slept,
In his quiet pipe the while;
Then, like a musical adept,
To blow the pipe his lips he wrinkled,
And green and blue his sharp eyes twinkled
Like a candle-flame where salt is sprinkled;
And ere three shrill notes the pipe uttered,
You heard as if an army muttered;
And the muttering grew to a grumbling;
And the grumbling grew to a mighty rumbling;
And out of the houses the rats came tumbling,
Great rats, small rats, lean rats, brawny rats,
Brown rats, black rats, grey rats, tawny rats,
Grave old plodders, gay young friskers,
Fathers, mothers, uncles, cousins,
Cocking tails and pricking whiskers,
Families by tens and dozens,
Brothers, sisters, husbands, wives—
Followed the Piper for their lives.

From street to street he piped advancing,
And step for step they followed dancing,
Until they came to the river Weser,
Wherein all plunged and perished!
– Save one who, stout as Julius Caesar,
Swam across and lived to carry
(As he, the manuscript he cherished)
To Rat-land home his commentary:
Which was, "At the first shrill notes of the pipe
I heard a sound as of scraping tripe,
And putting apples, wondrous ripe,
Into a cider-press's gripe:
And a moving away of pickle-tub-boards,
And a leaving ajar of conserve-cupboards,
And a drawing the corks of train-oil-flasks,
And a breaking the hoops of butter-casks;
And it seemed as if a voice
(Sweeter far than by harp or by psaltery
Is breathed) called out 'Oh, rats, rejoice!
The world is grown to one vast drysaltery!
So munch on, crunch on, take your nuncheon,
Breakfast, supper, dinner, luncheon!'
And just as a bulky sugar-puncheon,
All ready staved, like a great sun shone
Glorious scarce an inch before me,
Just as methought it said 'Come, bore me!'
– I found the Weser rolling o'er me."

Scuttle with the rats following the weird and wonderful Pied
Piper in this extract from a much-loved poem.

Kubla Khan
Samuel Taylor Coleridge

In Xanadu did Kubla Khan
A stately pleasure-dome decree:
Where Alph, the sacred river, ran
Through caverns measureless to man
Down to a sunless sea.
So twice five miles of fertile ground
With walls and towers were girdled round:
And there were gardens bright with sinuous rills,
Where blossomed many an incense-bearing tree;
And here were forests ancient as the hills,
Enfolding sunny spots of greenery.

But oh! that deep romantic chasm which slanted
Down the green hill athwart a cedarn cover!
A savage place! as holy and enchanted
As e'er beneath a waning moon was haunted
By woman wailing for her demon-lover!
And from this chasm, with ceaseless turmoil seething,
As if this earth in fast thick pants were breathing,
A mighty fountain momently was forced:
Amid whose swift half-intermitted burst

Huge fragments vaulted like rebounding hail,
Or chaffy grain beneath the thresher's flail:
And 'mid these dancing rocks at once and ever
It flung up momently the sacred river.
Five miles meandering with a mazy motion
Through wood and dale the sacred river ran,
Then reached the caverns measureless to man,
And sank in tumult to a lifeless ocean:
And 'mid this tumult Kubla heard from far
Ancestral voices prophesying war!

The shadow of the dome of pleasure
Floated midway on the waves;
Where was heard the mingled measure
From the fountain and the caves.
It was a miracle of rare device,
A sunny pleasure-dome with caves of ice!

A damsel with a dulcimer
In a vision once I saw:
It was an Abyssinian maid,
And on her dulcimer she played,
Singing of Mount Abora.
Could I revive within me
Her symphony and song,
To such a deep delight 'twould win me
That with music loud and long
I would build that dome in air,

That sunny dome! those caves of ice!
And all who heard should see them there,
And all should cry, Beware! Beware!
His flashing eyes, his floating hair!
Weave a circle round him thrice,
And close your eyes with holy dread,
For he on honey-dew hath fed
And drunk the milk of Paradise.

If you find it hard to learn a whole poem off by heart, don't give up. Sometimes even poets can't get to the end. Coleridge didn't finish this one as he was interrupted by "a person from Porlock".

A Lay Made About the Year Of The City CCCLX

Thomas Babbington Macaulay

XXI

And nearer fast and nearer
   Doth the red whirlwind come;
And louder still and still more loud,
   From underneath that rolling cloud,
Is heard the trumpet's war-note proud,
   The trampling, and the hum.
And plainly and more plainly
   Now through the gloom appears,
Far to left and far to right,
   In broken gleams of dark-blue light,
The long array of helmets bright,
   The long array of spears.

XXII

And plainly and more plainly,
   Above that glimmering line,
Now might ye see the banners
   Of twelve fair cities shine;
But the banner of proud Clusium
   Was highest of them all,
The terror of the Umbrian,
   The terror of the Gaul.

XXIII

And plainly and more plainly
   Now might the burghers know,
By port and vest, by horse and crest,
   Each warlike Lucumo.
There Cilnius of Arretium
   On his fleet roan was seen;
And Astur of the four-fold shield,
Girt with the brand none else may wield,
Tolumnius with the belt of gold,
And dark Verbenna from the hold
   By reedy Thrasymene.

XXIV

Fast by the royal standard,
   O'erlooking all the war,
Lars Porsena of Clusium
   Sat in his ivory car.
By the right wheel rode Mamilius,
   Prince of the Latian name;
And by the left false Sextus,
   That wrought the deed of shame.

XXV

But when the face of Sextus
   Was seen among the foes,
A yell that rent the firmament
   From all the town arose.
On the house-tops was no woman

But spat towards him and hissed,
No child but screamed out curses,
And shook its little fist.

XXVI
But the Consul's brow was sad,
And the Consul's speech was low,
And darkly looked he at the wall,
And darkly at the foe.
"Their van will be upon us
Before the bridge goes down;
And if they once may win the bridge,
What hope to save the town?"

XXVII
Then out spake brave Horatius,
The Captain of the Gate:
"To every man upon this earth
Death cometh soon or late.
And how can man die better
Than facing fearful odds,
For the ashes of his fathers,
And the temples of his gods,

It may seem strange, but in 1842 most people knew this poem off by heart.

The Rime of the Ancient Mariner
Samuel Taylor Coleridge

PART ONE
It is an ancient Mariner,
And he stoppeth one of three.
"By thy long grey beard and glittering eye,
Now wherefore stopp'st thou me?

The Bridegroom's doors are opened wide,
And I am next of kin;
The guests are met, the feast is set:
May'st hear the merry din."

He holds him with his skinny hand,
"There was a ship," quoth he.
"Hold off! unhand me, grey-beard loon!"
Eftsoons his hand dropped he.

He holds him with his glittering eye—
The Wedding Guest stood still,
And listens like a three years' child:
The Mariner hath his will.

The Wedding Guest sat on a stone:
He cannot choose but hear;
And thus spake on that ancient man,
The bright-eyed Mariner.

"The ship was cheered, the harbour cleared,
Merrily did we drop
Below the kirk, below the hill,
Below the lighthouse top.

The Sun came up upon the left,
Out of the sea came he!
And he shone bright, and on the right
Went down into the sea.

Higher and higher every day,
Till over the mast at noon—"
The Wedding Guest here beat his breast,
For he heard the loud bassoon.

The bride hath paced into the hall,
Red as a rose is she;
Nodding their heads before her goes
The merry minstrelsy.

The Wedding Guest he beat his breast,
Yet he cannot choose but hear;
And thus spake on that ancient man,
The bright-eyed Mariner.

"And now the STORM-BLAST came, and he
Was tyrannous and strong:
He struck with his o'ertaking wings,
And chased us south along.

With sloping masts and dipping prow,
As who pursued with yell and blow
Still treads the shadow of his foe,
And forward bends his head,
The ship drove fast, loud roared the blast,
And southward aye we fled.

And now there came both mist and snow,
And it grew wondrous cold:
And ice, mast-high, came floating by,
As green as emerald.

And through the drifts the snowy clifts
Did send a dismal sheen:
Nor shapes of men nor beasts we ken—
The ice was all between.

The ice was here, the ice was there,
The ice was all around:
It cracked and growled, and roared and howled,
Like noises in a swound!

At length did cross an Albatross:
Thorough the fog it came;
As if it had been a Christian soul,
We hailed it in God's name.

It ate the food it ne'er had eat,
And round and round it flew.
The ice did split with a thunder-fit;
The helmsman steered us through!

And a good south wind sprung up behind;
The Albatross did follow,
And every day, for food or play,
Came to the mariners' hollo!

In mist or cloud, on mast or shroud,
It perched for vespers nine;
Whiles all the night, through fog-smoke white,
Glimmered the white Moon-shine."

"God save thee, ancient Mariner!
From the fiends, that plague thee thus!—
Why look'st thou so?" — With my cross-bow
I shot the ALBATROSS.

This extract was chosen by Philip Pullman, who was one of the judges at the **Off By Heart** *final. Pullman is keen to remind people (or inform them for the first time) about the great ballads. "I heard it first at the age of eight, and felt myself transported with wonder. There must be other children like me out there who'd feel the same."*

The Lady of Shalott
Alfred, Lord Tennyson

PART 1

On either side the river lie
Long fields of barley and of rye,
That clothe the wold and meet the sky;
And thro' the field the road runs by
    To many-towered Camelot;
And up and down the people go,
Gazing where the lilies blow
Round an island there below,
    The island of Shalott.

Willows whiten, aspens quiver,
Little breezes dusk and shiver
Through the wave that runs for ever
By the island in the river
    Flowing down to Camelot.
Four grey walls, and four grey towers,
Overlook a space of flowers,
And the silent isle imbowers
    The Lady of Shalott.

By the margin, willow-veiled,
Slide the heavy barges trailed
By slow horses; and unhailed
The shallop flitteth silken-sailed
    Skimming down to Camelot:
But who hath seen her wave her hand?
Or at the casement seen her stand?
Or is she known in all the land,
    The Lady of Shalott?

Only reapers, reaping early
In among the bearded barley,
Hear a song that echoes cheerly
From the river winding clearly,
    Down to towered Camelot:
And by the moon the reaper weary,
Piling sheaves in uplands airy,
Listening, whispers "'Tis the fairy
Lady of Shalott."

PART 2
There she weaves by night and day
A magic web with colours gay.
She has heard a whisper say,
    A curse is on her if she stay
To look down to Camelot.
She knows not what the curse may be,
And so she weaveth steadily,

233

And little other care hath she,
    The Lady of Shalott.

And moving thro' a mirror clear
That hangs before her all the year,
Shadows of the world appear.
There she sees the highway near
    Winding down to Camelot:
There the river eddy whirls,
And there the surly village-churls,
And the red cloaks of market girls,
    Pass onward from Shalott.

Sometimes a troop of damsels glad,
An abbot on an ambling pad,
Sometimes a curly shepherd-lad,
Or long-haired page in crimson clad,
    Goes by to towered Camelot;
And sometimes thro' the mirror blue
The knights come riding two and two:
She hath no loyal knight and true,
The Lady of Shalott.

But in her web she still delights
To weave the mirror's magic sights,
For often thro' the silent nights
A funeral, with plumes and lights
    And music, went to Camelot:

Or when the moon was overhead,
Came two young lovers lately wed:
"I am half sick of shadows," said
      The Lady of Shalott.

PART 3
A bow-shot from her bower-eaves,
He rode between the barley-sheaves,
The sun came dazzling through the leaves,
And flamed upon the brazen greaves
      Of bold Sir Lancelot.
A red-cross knight for ever kneeled
To a lady in his shield,
That sparkled on the yellow field,
      Beside remote Shalott.

The gemmy bridle glittered free,
Like to some branch of stars we see
Hung in the golden Galaxy.
The bridle bells rang merrily
      As he rode down to Camelot:
And from his blazoned baldric slung
A mighty silver bugle hung,
And as he rode his armour rung,
      Beside remote Shalott.

All in the blue unclouded weather
Thick-jewelled shone the saddle-leather,
The helmet and the helmet-feather
Burned like one burning flame together,
　　As he rode down to Camelot.
As often thro' the purple night,
Below the starry clusters bright,
Some bearded meteor, trailing light,
　　Moves over still Shalott.

His broad clear brow in sunlight glowed;
On burnished hooves his war-horse trode;
From underneath his helmet flowed
His coal-black curls as on he rode,
　　As he rode down to Camelot.
From the bank and from the river
He flashed into the crystal mirror,
"Tirra lirra," by the river
　　Sang Sir Lancelot.

She left the web, she left the loom,
She made three paces thro' the room,
She saw the water-lily bloom,
She saw the helmet and the plume,
　　She looked down to Camelot.
Out flew the web and floated wide;
The mirror cracked from side to side;
"The curse is come upon me," cried
　　The Lady of Shalott.

Part 4

In the stormy east-wind straining,
The pale yellow woods were waning,
The broad stream in his banks complaining,
Heavily the low sky raining
   Over towered Camelot;
Down she came and found a boat
Beneath a willow left afloat,
And round about the prow she wrote
   The Lady of Shalott.

And down the river's dim expanse—
Like some bold seer in a trance,
Seeing all his own mischance—
With a glassy countenance
   Did she look to Camelot.
And at the closing of the day
She loosed the chain, and down she lay;
The broad stream bore her far away,
   The Lady of Shalott.

Lying, robed in snowy white
That loosely flew to left and right—
The leaves upon her falling light—
Through the noises of the night
   She floated down to Camelot:
And as the boat-head wound along
The willowy hills and fields among,

They heard her singing her last song,
    The Lady of Shalott.

Heard a carol, mournful, holy,
Chanted loudly, chanted lowly,
Till her blood was frozen slowly,
And her eyes were darkened wholly,
    Turned to towered Camelot.
For ere she reached upon the tide
The first house by the water-side,
Singing in her song she died,
    The Lady of Shalott.

Under tower and balcony,
By garden-wall and gallery,
A gleaming shape she floated by,
Dead-pale between the houses high,
    Silent into Camelot.
Out upon the wharfs they came,
Knight and burgher, lord and dame,
And round the prow they read her name,
    The Lady of Shalott.

Who is this? and what is here?
And in the lighted palace near
Died the sound of royal cheer;
And they crossed themselves for fear,

All the knights at Camelot:
But Lancelot mused a little space;
He said, "She has a lovely face;
God in his mercy lend her grace,
The Lady of Shalott."

Tennyson's poem was based loosely on Arthurian legend. It was particularly popular with pre-Raphaelite artists, many of whom painted various scenes from the poem.

Afterword
by Daisy Goodwin

At the age of nine, Winston Churchill was a great disappointment to his mother Jenny. He was not good at lessons, he was argumentative and he stuttered. But then one of Winston's teachers introduced him to Macaulay's *Lays of Ancient Rome* and encouraged him to learn them off by heart.

Churchill duly memorized all twelve-hundred lines and recited them at his mother's next society party, to her amazement. He launched into the lines that begin the *Lay of Horatio*:

> "Lars Porsena of Closium
>> By the Nine Gods he swore
> That the great house of Tarquin
>> Should suffer wrong no more.
> By the Nine Gods he swore it,
>> And named a trysting day,
> And bade his messengers ride forth,
> East and west and south and north,
>> To summon his array."

His mother realized, for perhaps the first time, that her son might become more than an embarrassment.

Perhaps it is not too much of a stretch to see a link between

Macaulay's stirring stanzas and the rhythmic cadences of Churchill's speeches to the nation in the darkest days of the Second World War.

Today's children are more likely to do Vicky Pollard than Macaulay as their party piece, and doubtless Britney cuts more ice in the playground than Wordsworth, but they lose out as a result. Learning a poem at an early age is an investment for the future. As T.S. Eliot said, you don't need to understand a poem to enjoy it.

A seven-year-old might miss every nuance of *Kubla Khan* or *Ozymandias* – but, learnt young, the poems will stay in the head for life, adding lustre to the good moments and illumination in the bad. Memorizing a poem means you own it.

As a child, I was paid by my grandmother to learn Shakespeare sonnets at 50p a pop. Back then the fringe benefit of a good memory was a steady supply of Maltesers; now I can call up "Bare ruin'd choirs, where late the sweet birds sang" every autumn and "Th' expense of spirit in a waste of shame is lust in action" every time I look at a tabloid newspaper.

Although rote learning of verse went out of fashion a generation ago, together with dates and tables, there is now a feeling among teachers and educators that this kind of performance-based learning has real benefits. It can be particularly useful for children with dyslexia.

A friend of mine, who is head of sixth form at a leading grammar school, says: "Young children have amazing recall;

they can quote song lyrics and comedy sketches verbatim. If you teach a child a poem orally, they can pick it up in an afternoon. That child may have problems reading, but by memorizing the poem they can approach it on the page with real confidence. The key is to make it a pleasure rather than a duty."

This is the key: learning poetry by heart should be fun, not another piece of homework. Starting very young, when the brain is at its most receptive, is essential.

I will never forget going to a primary school to give a talk on poetry and asking if the seven-year-olds knew any poems by heart. One little girl put her hand up and proceeded to recite, word-perfect, *The Night Mail* by W.H. Auden.

She may not have understood every line, but she certainly got the poem's rhythmic urgency, rocking from side to side with its locomotive beat:

This is the Night Mail crossing the border,
Bringing the cheque and the postal order,
Letters for the rich, letters for the poor,
The shop at the corner and the girl next door.

When she finished, her classmates gave her a round of applause. She told me that it was "really fun learning poems. The best bit is when everybody claps".

It is time to rebrand poetry as an achievement, not a soppy indulgence. To this end the BBC, together with my production company, Silver River, launched a poetry recital competition open to every child in the country between the ages of seven and eleven which formed the basis of the BBC2 film *Off By Heart*. The success of *Off By Heart* would not have been possible without the enthusiasm of the thousands of children who learnt poems, sometimes for the first time, as well as the dedication of all the teachers, parents, librarians and judges involved and the hard work of the whole team at BBC Learning, who organised the competition.

Off By Heart is modelled on similar schemes run in America and Ireland, where they have proved hugely popular. Last year more than 150,000 children took part in the contest in the United States. One teacher from Kansas City wrote: "Success in reciting poetry gives even reluctant learners a feeling of success in an area in which they have had little interest. I think it takes away some of the perceived difficulty and mystery of poetry for many of the students."

The competitors were equally enthusiastic. One state champion wrote: "Memorizing the poem gets it stuck in your head and your heart, so when you really understand the poem, it's not just saying it – it's like feeling the poem itself come from you."

One of the aims of the competition is to put pupils in direct contact with the nation's greatest poetry. A 2007 Ofsted report complained that across primary and secondary schools, too much poetry teaching was dull and unchallenging.

Indeed, after checking poetry teaching at eighty-six schools, the inspectors concluded that it was the worst-taught aspect of English.

This is not the teachers' fault: it is hard to instill a love of poetry in others if you have never learnt to love it yourself. The report also said that too few pupils were reading classic poems such as Wordsworth's *I wandered lonely as a cloud* or Coleridge's *Rime of the Ancient Mariner*.

Wordsworth features on the list of poems that children needed to learn for the *Off By Heart* competition, as well as Rudyard Kipling, Robert Burns, A.A. Milne, W.H. Davies and Benjamin Zephaniah. This may seem tough going for junior school pupils, but a hundred, or even fifty, years ago, poems of this length and complexity would have been learnt routinely by children of this age. Surely not such a challenge, then, for a generation raised on Nintendo.

Who knows how many hitherto unpromising nine-year-olds may discover a fluency and confidence that they never knew they possessed and find themselves on the path to greatness? Or, failing that, they will always have a way of passing the time in traffic jams.

This book contains all the poems that the children were asked to learn for the competition, plus many more. What these poems have in common is that they all gain an extra dimension when read aloud. Some of them come recommended by the likes of Seamus Heaney, Philip Pullman and Michael Rosen. We have arranged the poems in order of length and difficulty, so I suggest learning a poem from Section One to start with, and when that's been mastered, moving on to the poems in Sections Two and Three. "Difficulty" in this context means subject as well as length: younger children usually enjoy comic poems or poems that are firmly rooted in the physical, like *Alligator* by Grace Nichols, or even *The Listeners* by Walter De La Mare. Better to start them off with something they can visualize than an abstract poem like *The Tyger* by William Blake (the first stanza is fine but when you start getting into "awful symmetry", you lose most of the under-tens). Don't be afraid of encouraging children to learn longer poems; it is much easier for them than it is for you! One way of getting children to learn poetry (apart from straightforward bribery) is to do a sponsored versathon. Pick a long poem like *The Pied Piper of Hamelin* and sponsor the children at so much per line. It is a good way of raising money for charity and improving their minds at the same time.

Remember, it is easier to learn things if you are moving (what the experts call kinaesthetic learning). So if you want to memorize a poem, or you want to encourage a child to do so, take them for a walk. The poet Ruth Padel said that she learnt reams of poetry as a child while walking the dog. The more you associate poetry with pleasure rather than pain, the more likely it is to become a habit for life.

Daisy Goodwin

Starting as an Arts Producer at the BBC, Daisy devised the highly successful shows *Bookworm*, *The Nation's Favourite Poems*, *Looking Good* and *Home Front*. In 1998 Daisy moved to Talkback Productions as Head of Factual, quickly being promoted to Editorial Director. The three BAFTA nominated shows *House Doctor*, *Jamie's Kitchen* and *Grand Designs* as well as the hugely captivating *How Clean Is Your House?*, *Would Like to Meet* and *Your Money Or Your Life* are all the product of Daisy's pioneering mind.

In 2005 Daisy started Silver River, an independent production company, producing comedy, arts, documentary, period drama and factual entertainment. Credits include *Reader I Married Him*, a series about romantic fiction for BBC4, the food history series *The Supersizers Go. . .* for BBC2 and the comedy series *Pulling*, also for the BBC.

In addition to this, Daisy is a mother of two and editor of numerous poetry anthologies, including the bestseller *101 Poems That Could Save Your Life*. Daisy has also presented the BBC2 production of *Essential Poems (To Fall In Love With)* followed by *Essential Byron*, *Essential Poems for Britain* and *Essential Poems for Christmas*. In 2007 Daisy published *The Silver River*, a personal memoir and exploration of her Argentinian family's history. She is currently writing her first novel.

Index of First Lines

Index of Poets and Poems

Acknowledgments

John Agard: "Rat Race" Copyright © 2009 by John Agard.

Allan Ahlberg: "Please Mrs Butler" from *Please Mrs Butler* (Kestrel 1983, Puffin Books 1984) Copyright © Allan Ahlberg, 1983. Reproduced by permission of Penguin Books Ltd.

Maya Angelou: "Still I Rise" © Maya Angelou 1978. Reproduced from *The Complete Collected Poems* by Maya Angelou by kind permission of Virago, an imprint of Little, Brown Book Group.

W.H Auden: "Night Mail" from *W.H. Auden: Collected Poems* copyright © 1936 by W.H. Auden. Used by permission of Curtis Brown Ltd.

Pam Ayres: "Clive The Fearless Birdman" from *The Works* by Pam Ayres, published by BBC Books. © 1992 Pam Ayres. Reproduced by permission of Sheil Land Associates Ltd.

Hilaire Belloc: "The Frog" from *The Bad Child's Book of Beasts* © The Estate of Hilaire Belloc 1986; "Henry King", "Jim" and "Matilda" from *Cautionary Tales for Children* © The Estate of Hilaire Belloc 1907 all reproduced by permission of PFD (www.pfd.co.uk) on behalf of the Estate of Hilaire Belloc.

John Betjeman: "A Subaltern's Love-song" © John Betjeman by kind permission of the Estate of John Betjeman.

Charles Causley: "Timothy Winters" and "Colonel Fazackerley Butterworth-Toast" from *Collected Poems* (Macmillan, 1992) reprinted by permission of David Higham Associates.

John Clare: "Clock-a-Clay" and "First Love" reproduced with permission of Curtis Brown Group Ltd, London on behalf of Eric Robinson. Copyright © Eric Robinson 1984.

E.E. Cummings: "maggie and milly and molly and may" is reprinted from *Complete Poems 1904-1962* by E.E. Cummings, edited by George J. Firmage by permission of W.W. Norton & Company. Copyright © 1991 by the Trustees for the E.E. Cummings Trust and George James Frimage.

Roald Dahl: "Little Red Riding Hood and the Wolf" from *Revolting Rhymes* and "The Pig" from *Dirty Beasts*, both published by Jonathan Cape Ltd and Puffin Books, reproduced by permission of David Higham Associates Ltd.